'A TOILSOME TASK OF INDUSTRY'
Copper Mining and Smelting in Wales

By the same author:

O Fôn i Van Diemen's Land

Melinau Môn

Mynydd Parys

Eglwys Cyngar Sant Llangefni (guide book – English and Welsh)

Forty Years of Treading the Boards: a history of Theatr Fach, Llangefni (English and Welsh)

Sentenced to Hell: the story of men and women transported from north Wales, 1730–1878

'A Toilsome Task of Industry'

Copper Mining and Smelting in Wales

J. Richard Williams

Consultant editor:
John Mason BsC MPhil

First published in 2013

© Gwasg Carreg Gwalch 2013

Published with the financial support
of the Welsh Books Council

ISBN: 978-1-84527-403-0

Cover design: Welsh Books Council

Published by Gwasg Carreg Gwalch,
12 Iard yr Orsaf, Llanrwst, Wales LL26 0EH
tel: 01492 642031
fax: 01492 641502
email: books@carreg-gwalch.com
website: www.carreg-gwalch.com

Jonathan Roose (1731–1813) was born in Birchover, Derbyshire.

He died at eighty-two years old.

His gravestone in St Eleth's churchyard, Amlwch,
has a most fitting epitaph:

Among the throng of congregated dead
Of kindred men who's spirit hence are fled
Has lived one who's mind had long to bear
A toilsome task of industry and care
He first yon mountain wondrous riches found
First drew its mineral blessing from the ground.
He heard the miners first exhaulting shout
Then toiled near fifty years to guide its treasures out.

The curse of time will soon this stone decay
His name, his memory will pass away
Yet shall be left some monument behind
The mighty products of his mastermind
Those labour'd levels which he formed to draw.
The teemful waters to the vale below
And pillared caverns whence he drew the ore
Will long his genius shine when known his name no more.

to Hannah

so that she may learn about part of her Welsh heritage.

I am very much indebted to Jen Llywelyn
for her assistance and wise counsel.

Contents

Introduction

At almost the most northerly and southerly points of Wales are some of the most important remnants of our industrial past. Both Parys Mountain and Swansea were of major importance in the birth and death of the copper industry in Wales, but relatively few people are aware of how significant these and other much smaller sites were.

Little has been made of their contribution to the Industrial Revolution. Parys Mountain dominated the world copper market at one time, but in almost two and a half centuries only a handful of books have been written about it. Swansea's contribution has been better documented, but it is doubtful, for instance, whether the National Eisteddfod of Wales' Crown or Chair have been offered as a prize for poetry about the copper industry, whilst the coal miners and slate quarry men have fared better.

What little has been written about Parys Mountain and Swansea's Copperopolis can be summed up in the words of two literary giants of twentieth-century Wales: Bobi Jones and Dafydd Rowlands.

Of Parys Mountain, Bobi Jones said that it is a unique wilderness covered by blue, red, yellow and black spoil heaps, giving it a most 'attractive ugliness'.[1]

Dafydd Rowlands says of Pontardawe, in the Swansea Valley:

the place has changed so much,
You wouldn't recognise it by now.
Hooterless, furnaceless, and smokeless:
And the poison of the chemical works buried
    under the primroses.
'They' say that the village has improved.[2]

But where would we be without that industrial past? We should be grateful, perhaps, that we were not part of it. Conditions in the mines were bad, and wages were low. Small ventures never had a huge number of workers, and those who were involved usually had other jobs to help them survive financially. In much larger concerns, such as at Parys Mountain or in Swansea, where many were dependent on one source of income, industrial unrest was common. Most of the grievances were about lack of food and low wages, and the workers realised their strength lay in unity. After a poor harvest in 1792, copper workers from outside Swansea organised a protest march. In 1795 a strike was held at the Mines Royal in Neath. Three years later another was held at the Birmingham Copper Company works in Swansea. By 1808 many of the copper industry workers of Swansea had joined together to form a union: thirteen of the leaders were arrested and sent to prison on a charge of illegal conspiracy.

But it has to be accepted that the copper industry, with all its faults, helped shape Wales into what she is. What signs that remain should be prized. Long may our history live.

J. Richard Williams
Ynys Môn, Autumn 2012

---

[1] *Crwydro Môn*, Bobi Jones. (Llyfrau'r Dryw, 1957).
[2] *Cwm Tawe*, Hywel Teifi Edwards (ed.). (Gwasg Gomer, 1993).

Geological introduction:
John Mason BsC MPhil

The story of the mining and smelting of metals in Wales is long, complicated and fascinating, having its roots deep in prehistory and its tentacles pervading the evolution of the Welsh nation. There are certainly some conspicuous gaps here and there, but with every decade that passes, new research casts ever more light on such periods. However, there is one part of the tale that is not always told: the absolutely fundamental one of how the metal-ores came to be there in the first place, without which none of the rest would have been possible.

Ores are naturally-occurring minerals which, because of their metal contents or other useful physical properties, have intrinsic value when they occur in sufficient quantities and grades to be efficiently extracted. In today's terms, that means that they can be mined at financial profit. How a Bronze-Age copper miner would have defined ore-grade material is less certain but ease of working and ease of smelting would surely have been key factors.

As with many of the base metals, copper is relatively uncommon in nature in its pure metallic form, and instead most of its ores are sulphides – combinations of copper and other metals with sulphur. Of these, the one most frequently met with in Wales is the brassy-yellow chalcopyrite ($CuFeS2$): although many other copper-bearing sulphides have been identified in recent years, there are few instances where they were important Welsh ores. But all were formed in similar ways: primarily, they crystallised from superheated and pressurised metal-rich brines circulating deep below the Earth's surface. The mechanism by which sulphides precipitate from solution varies: it may occur due to temperature or pressure-changes, or when such solutions encounter reactive rocks such as limestones, the resultant reactions changing the ability of the solution to carry dissolved metals.

Like most metal sulphides, chalcopyrite is a stable chemical compound when present deep underground, isolated from the effects of air and water. However, closer to the surface these agents of weathering are able to react with the chalcopyrite and the reactions result in the formation of a range of secondary copper minerals. Of these, the most familiar are the green and blue carbonates, malachite and azurite respectively: malachite is widespread in Wales and was in some instances worked as an ore in its own right.

How the primary chalcopyrite-bearing ore deposits came into being is a subject that still attracts much research, for it interweaves with the geological evolution of Wales itself, a narrative that is far from complete. However, we do have a reasonable overall picture of the processes that formed and shaped this mountainous country, now at a high northern latitude, from its beginnings as a group of volcanic islands situated deep in the southern hemisphere, hundreds of millions of years ago.

It was volcanic activity back then, at the boundary between the Cambrian and Ordovician periods, some 488 million years ago, that led to the formation of the largest copper deposit known in Wales – unworked, and discovered in the 1960s in Coed y Brenin, north of Dolgellau. Estimated to contain some 200 million tonnes of ore grading at an average of 0.3 per cent copper – that's over 600,000 tonnes of copper metal – the deposit was formed deep in the roots of a volcanic island. The heat from the deep magma-chamber drove convective cells through which hot waters circulated, leaching copper and other metals from the rocks. As the high-level intrusive rocks immediately under the volcano cooled down, the fluids then redeposited the copper as sulphides along numerous small cracks. The resultant orebody, therefore, was a mass of igneous rock with the copper minerals disseminated throughout it. Mining would have required large-scale opencast methods at a location within the Snowdonia National Park, but this was only one of the reasons that the project was shelved: at the time there were larger tonnages and better grades available in similar deposits at various overseas locations.

Also associated with this volcanism was the formation of several pipelike bodies, at a higher topographical level, filled with explosively shattered rock cemented together by minerals including copper-ores. These are thought to have formed due to the explosive contact of large volumes of ground-water with magma, resulting in the sudden generation of vast amounts of superheated steam. Several such pipes are known, of which one has been worked at the Glasdir copper mine.

The theme of volcanic activity and copper mineralisation continued through the Ordovician Period, with a particularly important phase of mineral deposit formation being associated with the development, some 460 million years ago, of a large volcanic caldera, in what is now the Snowdon district. Some of the eruptions associated with the caldera were gigantic by historical standards: one is thought to have produced some sixty cubic kilometres of volcanic ash (compared to an estimated 2.79 cubic km for the catastrophic 1980 Mount St Helens eruption). Down in the depths of the caldera, as the eruptive cycle waned, hot groundwaters circulating through the rocks dissolved metals, redepositing them as ores, such as chalcopyrite, in a series of lodes. Lodes are fractures that traverse the rocks, maybe a metre in thickness, maybe ten metres exceptionally, that are filled with minerals including various ores. They may extend across country for hundreds of metres or tens of kilometres: depth-wise they may go down a kilometre or more. They may be vertical or inclined. Compared to disseminated deposits like Coed y Brenin, they typically contain lower tonnages of ore but at much higher grades.

The lodes of the Snowdon district are typically 1–2 metres in thickness and often close to vertical, so that the surface opencut workings where ores have been removed are steep-sided slots in the landscape, with associated heaps of rusty-coloured spoil that consist of rock-fragments and minerals regarded at the time as worthless. Deeper mining was facilitated by sinking shafts and driving gently-inclined levels to allow the water to drain out naturally or, at greater depths, to the pumping-sumps situated at the bases of shafts from where it could be pumped to surface.

Chalcopyrite-bearing lodes of Ordovician age occur in other parts of Wales. There are scattered, minor occurrences in the St David's district of Pembrokeshire and a more important belt of lodes occurs in southern Snowdonia, from Barmouth up past Dolgellau towards Trawsfynydd. This is the well-known Dolgellau Gold-belt, where a number of historically important gold-mines are situated, but the lodes were also worked for copper in places. They traverse both igneous and sedimentary rocks and research suggests that they were formed by the generation of mineralising fluids during the metamorphism (changes in mineralogy and chemistry brought about by high temperatures and pressures) of deeply-buried rocks that to this day remain well below the surface.

During the succeeding Silurian Period, volcanism was much more localised in extent, but it was associated with the formation of Wales' biggest mined copper deposit – Parys

Mountain on Anglesey. Here, the chalcopyrite and other ore-minerals were deposited from 'black-smokers' – vents on the sea-bed from which boiling hot mineral-laden waters gushed, the sulphides precipitating out as myriad tiny dark particles, hence the 'smoke' effect. The particles settled to the sea-bed around the vents, accumulating as sulphide-rich muds, building up into cones and periodically collapsing and sliding, and as vent activity died out, being buried by countless layers of sediment, to form what is known as a 'volcanogenic massive sulphide' deposit. The orebody was worked opencast, in this case not because it was disseminated through the rock but because it was high-grade and massive in extent.

Elsewhere in Wales, volcanism was absent during the Silurian Period (with the exception of a small area in south-western Wales) and sediments - muds, silts and sands – accumulated on the bed of the marine Welsh Basin. At the close of the Silurian Period, the Basin had become filled with sediments and the transition from a marine to a subaerial environment occurred into the succeeding Devonian Period which commenced some 397 million years ago. By this time, Wales had drifted northwards and was heading towards the southern tropics: other small landmasses were similarly drifting northwards and collisions between them led to deformation, such as folding, in the sedimentary and volcanic rocks alike.

Central Wales – the district inland from Aberystwyth – consists at surface of extensive Silurian and late Ordovician sedimentary rocks and these are host to another system of lodes, some of which contained sufficient chalcopyrite to be worked for copper, although lead, zinc and silver were at most mines the most important products. The lodes are up to several metres in width and are filled with shattered rock-fragments cemented by quartz and sulphides. This mineralisation occurred after the folding episode mentioned above and it formed in several phases, with existing lodes reactivating and later minerals forming veins crosscutting earlier minerals. Dating suggests that the earliest Central Wales mineralisation began in the Devonian Period, further phases occurred in the Carboniferous Period and the latest phase may have been as recent as the Triassic or Jurassic, just a couple of hundred million years ago. The mineralising fluids originated via a variety of sources, including from metamorphism of rocks at depth and from the deep sedimentary basins that formed offshore during the Triassic and Jurassic Periods, where metalliferous so-called 'oilfield-brines' developed and were expelled as the basins deepened.

Triassic and Jurassic oilfield-brines were also responsible for extensive mineralisation in the limestones of Lower Carboniferous age (360–330 million years old) that are to be found in north-east and south Wales. In general, the lodes that crisscrossed the limestones contained only traces of chalcopyrite, but at one locality, Great Orme, near Llandudno, an important copper-deposit was formed. Here, hot, saline mineralising fluids deposited abundant dolomite, a carbonate of calcium and magnesium, together with abundant chalcopyrite.

After the Jurassic Period, significant primary mineralising activity appears to have largely ceased. By this time, Wales – along with the rest of the British Isles – had crossed the equator and was drifting northward. Having been incorporated into the supercontinent of Pangaea at the end of the Carboniferous, the Cretaceous Period (145–65 million years ago) saw that continent rifting apart as the Atlantic Ocean started to form. The rifting continued throughout the succeeding Cenozoic era (65 million years ago–recent) and is ongoing today. Extensive volcanic activity, 60–50 million years ago, accompanied the rifting, leading to the formation of the extensive province of volcanic rocks across western Scotland and Northern Ireland. Large-scale uplifting of the Earth's crust affected many parts of north-west Europe, with Wales becoming an elevated landmass. At the time, Earth was experiencing a hothouse-type climate, with average temperatures more than 6°C warmer than the present day, which set the scene for a period of deep, tropical-style weathering of Wales' rocks and mineral deposits alike.

The weathering-episode, ongoing for several million years, almost certainly endowed all of Wales' copper-deposits, disseminated, massive, pipes or lodes, with enriched zones of secondary copper minerals. However, in only a few cases have such zones been exploited. The reason for that is down to climate change. Some 30 million years ago, the hothouse-type climate cooled into a more temperate phase, and then, starting about 15 million years ago, temperatures fell away steeply, culminating in the glacial-interglacial cycles that began to affect Wales a couple of million years ago. Glacial ice is a phenomenally-powerful agent of mechanical weathering, stripping away layer after layer of rock: the Welsh landscape of today has been carved by several successive glaciations, the last one reaching its maximum extent 18,000 years ago and only ending some 10,000 years ago. It is likely that glacial erosion ground away the zones of secondary enrichment over most copper deposits, with parts of just a few, such as Great Orme, remaining.

Weathering continues today, with copper-staining frequently found on the surfaces of chalcopyrite-bearing boulders in mine-waste, for instance: however, the only example of economic concentrations of copper forming in the period since the last glaciation is the very unusual Turf

Copper deposit, near Dolgellau. Here, copper, weathering out from the Coed y Brenin disseminated orebody and transported in dissolved form by groundwaters, encountered a peat-bog with its highly reducing chemical environment. The copper precipitated out, often as the native metal, entirely replacing fragments of organic matter such as leaves and acorns to form a rich and easily-extractable source of the metal. It is a neat ending to this near 500 million years long story to note that Wales' youngest important copper deposit was formed by the weathering of its oldest!

John Mason
2012, Machynlleth

1

Copper

During the summer months of 2010, the name of the small and apparently unsafe copper and gold mine of San José, near Copiapo in northern Chile, was heard once more in Wales. In the nineteenth century Copiapo was a familiar name to Swansea copper workers and sailors as a source of much raw material brought into Wales to be smelted. When it reappeared, it brought present-day copper mining to the attention of the world as thirty-three miners were trapped 700 metres underground by a collapsed roof. Thankfully, after a sixty-nine day ordeal, all were eventually rescued – though twenty-three of their colleagues had died in the collapse. This brought mining Health and Safety issues to the fore, and once again reminded everyone what 'a toilsome task of industry' copper mining can be.

Some metals can occur in nature in almost pure form, known as 'native'. Prehistoric man found native gold as nuggets and flakes glinting in streams. Gold is very soft. Prehistoric man worked it into jewellery, but it was too soft to replace stone or bone tools. Some copper is also found in native form. It, too, was workable, but was hard enough to use as axes – though they needed frequent sharpening.

Rare nuggets of native copper were found among copper ores. Applying fire to the ores liberated the copper as molten metal. This discovery, about 7,000 years ago, led to the Copper Age – about 4500 BC to 3500 BC. Why have few people heard of the Copper Age? Because a second discovery was soon made: that adding one part of tin to nine parts of copper produced the alloy bronze, which is much harder than copper. At last metal could replace stone.

Copper, as the main component of bronze, was plentiful. The ores occurred often at the earth's surface.

Copper was the first metal used on a large scale by man. As it is a multifunctional metal, it has been used for at least 9,000 years. It was relatively easy to work with, and so much better than any other clay/stone material for making eating and drinking vessels, ornaments or weapons. Throughout history, it has been used for a variety of purposes.

The *ankh* was chosen by Greek philosophers as the sign to represent copper. It is based on the Egyptian hieroglyph meaning 'eternal life' and is used to represent the goddess Venus and the planet of the same name. It is also the female symbol, associated with the goddess Aphrodite, and her mythical connections with the island of Cyprus, from where the Latin *Cuprum* originates, and where copper was extensively mined in Roman times.

Copper is a chemical element, with the chemical symbol *Cu*, the atomic number 29 in the Periodic Table of the Elements, an atomic weight of 63.54, and a specific gravity of 8.92 at 20 degrees Celsius. The melting point of copper is 1083.4 degrees Celsius and it boils at a temperature of 2567 degrees Celsius. On Moh's Hardness Scale, copper registers at between 2.5 and 3, which means that it is harder than a fingernail but softer than a steel pocket knife.

Copper ores deposited from hot solutions moving through the rocks are especially common in area where volcanic activity has occurred. They are found worldwide, but 90 per cent of the main reserves are from four particular areas: the Great Basin of western United States of America, Zambia, Central Canada, and the mountainous Andes regions of Chile and Peru, South America. Antarctica also has huge copper ore deposits, but as mining there was prohibited in 1991 for the next fifty years, supplies are untouchable.

Copper was first discovered in the Middle East about 9,000 years ago. Smelting sites dating back to 4,500 BC have been discovered in present-day Egypt, Israel and Jordan, for example at the Kirbat Hamra Ifdan Foundry in southern Jordan, in which hammers and axes were found in some of its seventy rooms. Copper was widely used by the Sumerians and Chaldeans of Mesopotamia about 5,000 to 6,000 years ago. Their skills were acquired by the Egyptians at roughly the same time, and their use of the much harder bronze to make weapons, armour, tools and sculptures showed their knowledge and skill in using and utilising copper. Amongst the treasures of Tutankhamun were found bronze sculptures of a dog, snake, scimitar, spatula, candlesticks and a trumpet.

From roughly the same area but a little later came the Dead Sea Scrolls, discovered by a Bedouin goat-herd in 1947. A later discovery, in 1952, was a scroll inscribed on a thin sheet of copper mixed with a small amount of tin. Although scholars believe that the information written on the copper is about a lost treasure, it is thought to be a hoax.

Copper-casting happened in Thailand, south-east Asia, in 4,000 BC, and in Turkey in 3,000 BC. Copper objects from China and Hindustan, India, have been found. They have proved difficult to date but are thought to be from the Third Millennium BC. A complete Iron Age metal-smelting site has been discovered in Cyprus and the written history of the works show that bronze and brass (another alloy of copper) were produced there soon after copper was discovered on the island.

Slowly, metal-working skills filtered into Europe. When the Bell-Beaker people – so called because of the pottery vessels that were used and left in their round burial chambers – migrated to Britain (around 2,500 BC) they brought many skills with them and are acknowledged as the first metal-working people in Britain. On gaining knowledge of how to process metals from the Balkan and Mediterranean peoples, they travelled to central and northern Europe in search of a source and supply of copper and tin with which to make bronze. Amongst their earliest remains in Britain are those found in a burial site at Charmy Down, near Bath in south-west England, which included a bronze dagger; a flat copper axe-head has been found near Old Cleeve, Somerset, suggesting that the copper ore deposits of the Quantock Hills, near Nether Stowey, had been discovered and were being made use of.

When it was found that adding 10 per cent tin to copper produced the harder bronze alloy, tool and weapon production increased, and when it became common knowledge that the addition of lead to the alloy bronze improved its quality even more, buckets, cooking utensils, shields and swords were produced in ever-increasing numbers. In 1870, at Wick, near Stogursey in Somerset, a hoard of damaged copper axes, spearheads, swords and copper ingots was found, which, most probably, had been kept to melt down and re-cast.

The Anglo-Saxons became skilled smiths, making use of gold, silver and iron. Pure copper was little-used by them except for coinage, though bronze, and the other copper alloy, brass, became popular and much-used.

By the late sixteenth century, the early years of the Industrial Revolution, there was a higher demand for raw materials. Ulrich Fosse, a German who worked in the Cumberland copper mines, smelted 560 tons of copper ore in forty weeks. In the seventeenth and eighteenth centuries, it was possible to remove impurities (calcining) from the ore at a much quicker rate, and at the Llandore Works, Swansea, calcining copper became a speciality of one part of the works. There were also thirty-seven smelting furnaces for copper, lead and silver, and a refining and testing house on site as well.

In 1749 the Mines Royal at Neath Abbey, south Wales, was able to smelt 230 tons of copper ore in a week, which produced 18 tons of copper. Production on such a scale required thirty-eight furnaces and 315 tons of coal. Because of the proximity of a supply of good coal, the Swansea area became a major centre for the copper industry. In 1714 unrefined copper cake cost £100 per ton (equivalent to £7,659 in 2011 currency values). Plates of copper from Swansea were £140/150 per ton (£10,722/£11,488 in 2011) compared to the price of best-quality Swedish copper of £168 per ton in 1694 (£14,695 in 2011). With a production rate of about 100 tons per annum, this was very expensive compared with 2011 prices – which are considered to be at their highest levels. Swansea also had a port and was able to maximise all opportunities to import ore from Cornwall and beyond. With the use of steam pumps to remove water from mines, Cornwall had become a leading supplier of ore to Swansea.

Copper is malleable and can be shaped or formed, when hot or cold, without splitting. It can be compressed into a sheet of 1/500 inch thickness. It is also a very ductile metal and a 4-inch thick bar can be heated, rolled and drawn out into a wire, no thicker than a human hair, of up to and over 2,000,000 yards in length.

A yield of 4.4 lbs of copper per 2240 lbs of ore (the imperial ton, as used in the UK) is needed before it is economically viable to separate the ore from rock. Of all the copper produced in the world, the majority is used for electrical applications. Being an excellent conductor of electricity, copper is used in generators, transformers, motors and cables to conduct electricity efficiently, and as a very efficient conductor of heat in the manufacture of refrigerators, heaters and cooking utensils. It is also used to provide circuitry, wiring and contacts for personal computers, televisions and mobile phones.

Another of the benefits of copper is that it is resistant to corrosion. If left in a damp atmosphere it will lose its reddish/orange colour and will become covered by a layer or patina of light green (called verdigris), which stops any further corrosion.

Copper is also used in buildings, for plumbing, roofing and cladding. Copper helps make light and durable maintenance-free structures that are long-lasting and fully recyclable. Trains, cars and lorries use up to 7 per cent of the copper produced annually. High-grade or high-purity copper wires carry the current from the battery throughout the vehicle to equipment such as lights, central locking, in-car computers and satellite navigation systems. Electric trams in cities such as Manchester, Sheffield and Croydon provide clean, efficient transport powered by electric motors. The overhead contact wires are either copper-silver or copper-cadmium alloys. Copper has known antibacterial effects, and surfaces made with copper can help to reduce the spread of disease in hospitals and healthcare facilities. The remaining 3 per cent is used for coins, sculptures, musical instruments and cooking utensils.

The table below shows what percentage of the copper produced in the USA is used in various branches of their domestic industries:

Construction: plumbing and electrical wire	50.6%
Electrical and electronic products: generators, electrical devices etc	19.3%
Consumer goods and general products: coins, cooking utensils, refrigerators, cash registers etc	10.7%
Industrial machinery and equipment	8.9%
Transportation equipment: cars, submarines, trains, etc	10.5%
TOTAL	**100.0%**

(Source: Copper Development Association (figures for 2006), www.copperinfo.com/index/html)

The price of copper is about £2.80 per pound (March 2011), which reflects its availability. The price of gold (£12,108 per pound in March 2011) and silver (£296 per pound in March 2011) reflect their scarcity. Gold is still too rare and expensive to replace copper commercially, making copper a more economical material for use in industry. In the building industry a newly-built building/house of an area of 2,200 square feet includes roughly 450 lbs of copper; a car contains between 50 and 80 lbs of copper, and a Boeing 727 aeroplane includes 9,000 lbs of copper. It should also be remembered that copper, like aluminium and iron, can be effectively recycled without any loss of quality, and it is believed that at least 80 per cent of all the copper ever mined is still in use.

Copper is also an important and indispensable nutrient for plants and animals. In animals, including humans, it is stored in the liver and is an essential nutrient that plays a role in the production of haemoglobin, myelin, collagen and melanin. Only a small amount is needed, and anyone with a large accumulation of copper in the liver or brain could suffer from Wilson's disease or Menkes' disease. A copper deficiency could lead to anaemia, low body temperature, bone fractures and osteoporosis, loss of pigment from the skin, and thyroid disorders. Foods that contain copper include oysters, liver, cereals, shellfish, dark green leafy vegetables, nuts and chocolate.

2

Bronze Age man and cow find copper in Llandudno's Happy Valley!

Seen from afar, Llandudno's Great Orme (in Welsh, *Pen-y-Gogarth* – *'gogarth'* is a Viking word meaning 'serpent') appears to be a solid mass of carboniferous limestone. Rising to 207 metres above sea level, it seems to be an island separated from the mainland. Appearances can be deceptive, and The Orme, as it is locally known, is, in reality, a 'tombolo' (from the Latin *tumulus*, meaning 'mound'), an 'island' that is attached to the mainland by a narrow piece of land. As in many other Carboniferous Limestone masses the Great Orme has a natural maze of internal caves, springs and shafts.

The Great Orme consists of a layered sequence of limestones alternating with thin shale-bands, underlaid by a massive sandstone. These rocks were deposited in shallow, warm seas that covered the area in Lower Carboniferous times, about 350 million years ago. The sea-bed was later uplifted by earth-movements to become land, in its present position. The limestone is of a porous, brown appearance that is partly due to the replacement of its major constituent, calcite (calcium carbonate) by dolomite (calcium magnesium carbonate). This process is known as dolomitisation. The dolomitised limestones are intensively mineralised along fractures and in the abundant open cavities.

The copper mineralisation is developed within an area in which numerous steeply inclined faults cut the geological succession, with the best ores having occurred in the thickest beds of limestone. The Great Orme Copper Mine is extremely important in geological terms because it is where the first UK example of the "copper-dolomite association", an important worldwide class of mineral deposits, was recognised. This type of mineral deposit forms when hot, saline mineralising fluids become magnesium-rich and sulphur-poor, and, where they encounter limestone sequences, they deposit dolomite. Should the fluids circulate through certain deeply-buried rocks (such as volcanics), they may take copper into solution, which then combines with the remaining sulphur to form the copper-iron sulphide, chalcopyrite, which crystallises on the dolomite.

Chalcopyrite readily reacts with ground waters, derived from rainfall, in areas close to surface. At Great Orme this reaction has been particularly intense, due to the extremely porous nature of the ground. Chalcopyrite is often altered to the copper carbonate, malachite, which formerly occurred at Great Orme in sufficient amounts to be mined as a copper ore in its own right. Malachite is a conspicuous mineral, forming bright green crusts and thin stains, with, more rarely, the deep blue copper carbonate, azurite. In places, when the mine was at work, copper as a native metal was reported, occurring as branched groups of crystals. In the post-1845 period, when official figures for mineral production were kept, the Great Orme copper mines produced well over 25,000 tons of ore. Since miners have dug away at the deposit for over 3500 years, it is anybody's guess as to what the total production was – but it would have significantly exceeded this amount.

Again due to the heat, the limestone surrounding the veins of ore went through a chemical change, with the calcium being replaced by magnesium. A combination of calcium and magnesium became magnesium limestone or dolorite, which is softer than calcium limestone. Copper was

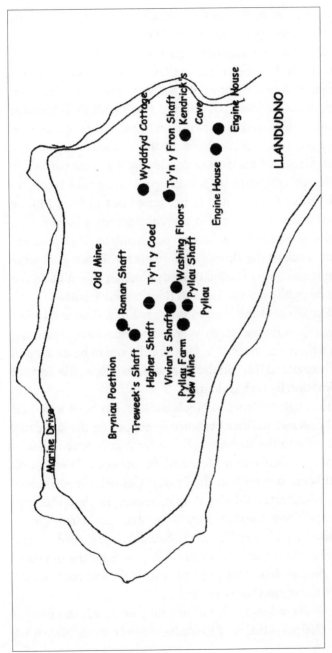

Great Orme copper mines

also exposed on the surface, which made the work of the later Bronze Age miners relatively easy.

Although investigations on the Orme began in 1976, comparatively little would be known of the Great Orme (Bronze Age) Copper Mine but for the fact that Llandudno's Town Council and the Welsh Development Agency approved a scheme in 1987 to landscape an abandoned and derelict site in the Pyllau Valley on the Great Orme, with a view to developing it as a car park.

Before any work on the car park site could begin, an underground survey had to be carried out. Ashton Mining Consultants were awarded the contract for a survey. The results showed the existence of chambers and passages dating back to the Bronze Age. Plans for the car park were abandoned and a feasibility study to open the mine to the general public was carried out. Results were positive.

The Great Orme Mines Company Ltd was set up in 1989 to carry out the study's recommendations. Planning permission was granted in 1990 for the site to be developed and expanded for public use and to allow for further exploration by archaeologists.

Although evidence of Neolithic Man has been found on the headland, positive evidence of copper on the site dates back only to the Bronze Age. Bronze Age copper mines in Britain and Ireland are few and far between: West Cork, south-west Ireland – in the Mount Gabriel, Canshanavoe, Ross Island area; Alderley Edge, Cheshire, England; Nant yr Eira and Cwm Ystwyth; Parys Mountain; and Great Orme, Llandudno, Gwynedd, which could be described as the 'jewel in the crown'. It is quite different from the others in that the ore found and mined is in fairly soft rock, which made the miners' work easier.

Discovered in 1976, but not fully explored, the Bronze Age Copper Mine at Llandudno merely confirmed what many had taken to be fact for many years. To study and properly survey the mine meant that over 100,000 tonnes of waste material from the eighteenth- and nineteenth-century works had to be removed. Underneath were found entrances to a site mined over 3,500 years ago. So far, almost 4 miles of tunnels have been explored, but it is estimated that another 6 miles are there to be discovered.

Working conditions during the Bronze Age period must have been damp, dark and difficult. Some of the miners had to work at depths of up to 70 metres below ground where some passages were very narrow – so narrow that only a small child could have worked in them. Due to the restrictive size and depths of the tunnels, a lack of oxygen may well have hampered working and prevented the miners from using candles or their animal oil and fat lamps. Some sort of ventilation needed to be provided, as an adequate supply of air was needed for the fires.

Charcoal remains from fires lit against the rocks have also been found. This indicates that fire-setting was used to expand the rock which, on cooling, would crack and the removed ore taken to the surface to be further crushed and washed before being smelted. The annular rings of the charcoal remains are well spaced out and show that the trees were coppiced to induce faster growth. Evidence of fire-setting has been found at a depth of 65 metres, which means that a complicated ventilation system would have been set up in the passages. Waste materials, known as 'deads', would be piled high in some shafts and levels to regulate the flow of air in the mine.

Stones (diorite, dolerite and basalt-igneous rocks) from nearby beaches were found inside the caverns, ranging in size from 4 to a massive 64 lbs. These were used as hammers. Over 30,000 animal bones have also been found, which were used as scraping tools. The majority of these were cattle bones, but sheep, goat, deer and even wild boar bones have been discovered. Some of them were stained green by malachite, having been underground for 3,000 years.

When the ore was brought to the surface, limestone had to be removed by crushing. Then it was smelted in a primitive kiln at an estimated temperature of 1,100 degrees Celsius. More charcoal was needed to fuel the kiln, and air pumped in. Tin would have been added to the molten copper to make bronze, and whilst still in a liquid state, the alloy was poured into moulds of different shapes.

It has been estimated that during the Bronze Age period of the industry around 1,769 tons of copper was produced in Llandudno. Much of the local production was used for domestic and ornamental work, but some was used in the production of bronze (copper + 10 per cent tin), which was a much harder alloy for the production of tools and weapons. Other theories about Llandudno's Bronze Age copper include the belief that up to ten million objects could have been produced there. The mines may well have produced a surplus of copper, which might have been exported from the area to south-west England, and to Cornwall in particular, where a supply of tin for the production of bronze was readily obtained.

No evidence of any later working of the mines during the Iron Age has come to light, and though Roman remains and articles have been found close by, no evidence of mine working survives from the time of the Roman occupation.

Between 1692 and 1881, however, much further work was carried out in the mines. During this period tons of waste rubble from new workings were thrown onto the Bronze Age site, hiding much precious evidence. In 1692 a twenty-one year lease was granted to Sir Thomas Mostyn from Edward Thomas Prees to work the site near Maes-yfacrell at a rent of 10/- a year and a royalty payment of 17/- per ton of ore mined.

In 1701 Sir Roger Mostyn leased mines on and under his lands at the south-eastern end of 'Llandudno Mountain' for twenty-one years to a small consortium of London merchants. These included John Cooper, Joseph Cope, Leonard Fletcher, Thomas Fryer and John Perry, who in 1694 had formed the Welsh Copper Company.

Richard Manley of Chester, and his relative William Manley of London, leased land for another twenty-one years from Thomas Herring, Bishop of Bangor in 1738 for the purpose of copper mining.

On his 'Plan of the Bay & Harbour of Conway in Caernarvonshire', published in 1748, Lewis Morris shows the copper mine on the Orme. In his 'Observations relating to the Improvements that might be made', he notes:

> There was formerly a great Copper Mine at Llandudno … which now lies under Water; but it might without much Difficulty be recovered, by proper Engines: until a great Level be brought up, for which the Place is well situated. Mine-works, lying thus on the Sea-side, are, upon many Accounts, much preferable to those in Inland Parts.[1]

In 1761 Sir Roger Mostyn leased land to Francis Smedley, and Anthony and Henry Steeple of Holywell, and they are known to have worked in the mining industry in Flintshire on condition they paid him a royalty of one seventh of the ore mined. John Ewer, the then Bishop of Bangor, leased part of the bishopric's land to John Bagnall of Erleigh Court, Sonning, Berkshire in 1774. Thomas Pennant was a visitor in 1773 and was quite impressed by what he saw – in particular, the presence of such a number of shafts and their depth.

The Mostyn lease of 1761 had expired by 1782 and another was granted to John Lloyd of Wigfair, Denbighshire, a lawyer and sometime Member of Parliament for Flintshire who was also known as 'The Philosopher'. He secured rights to erect buildings and build an engine on the site of the mine and also to construct a quay for the shipping of coal, ore and timber. Another condition was that at least six men would work the mine for nine months of the year. This lease was made out to Lloyd who, in fact, was acting on behalf of others, including William Bridge of Amlwch, Anglesey, and the Reverend John Ellis of Caernarvon, who sub-let the lease again to a group of unqualified and unskilled workers. By October of the same year, Bridge, Ellis and Lloyd had also leased the mine on the bishopric's land.

Bridge was a quick worker. On 29 March 1783 he signed a lease for seven years at Ty'n y Coed Mine, as well as at Llwyn Helyg, from Elizabeth Williams of Ty'n y coed. He later increased the period of the lease to twenty-one years. The mine, on Mostyn land, was known as the New Mine – but was not very active or productive. In the same year, Lord Bulkeley granted a twenty-one year lease to Lord Penrhyn, William Roe and Thomas Smyth of Liverpool. They spent £300 in the next three years, but little mining took place until 1833, when the land was granted to The New Mine.

Between 1793 and 1801 the Macclesfield Company mined ore for the Llandudno Mine Company and paid a one eighth royalty to John Warren and then to William Cleaver, bishops of Bangor. Ore worth £4,521 was sold at a profit of £1,125 to the Swansea smelters. This was a prosperous period for all concerned. Even the miners looked to the future. They established schools on the Orme at Pen y Buarth and Tŷ Coch, and paid a salary of £30 per annum to the schoolmaster.

By the end of the century, the two mines of Llandudno – the 'Old' and 'New' Mines – were working, and employing between 300 and 400 men – most of the local workforce. In the early years of the nineteenth century, the two mines were working in competition with one another. The Old Mine was on land controlled by the Bishop of Bangor to the north of the Orme including the site of the Bronze Age workings, and the New Mine on land owned by Lord Mostyn on the southern parts of the Orme.

The next Bishop of Bangor, Henry William Majendie, in 1812 appointed an agent to receive any royalty payments due from the Macclesfield Company for mining on the bishopric's land. Samuel Worthington (1760–1842) of Llwyn Onn, Llandegai, near Bangor, who had worked in the Penrhyn Slate Quarries, Bethesda, was the agent entrusted to do the work. He later took out a lease on the Old Mine. By 1825 he had taken over the mine, 700 acres of land and a royalty payment of one eighth on a lease from the bishopric. Samuel's sons, Archibald and William, took over the lease for their lifetime in 1837. They employed Jonathan Rawling, a Cornishman, as their agent. The mined ore from this period was sold mainly to the Mona and Parys Mine Companies in Amlwch, but also to other companies in Swansea. Between 1825 and 1833, their company made a loss of £3,476; between 1834 and 1835 a further loss of £1,824 was made, due mainly to so much work needing to be done on the shafts and on buying pumping equipment. However, in the period of 1836–1840 this turned in a very healthy profit of £11,973, and from 1825 to 1844 an overall profit of £7,400 was declared.

John Williams was mine agent at the Old Mine and author of a report on the mine and its facilities in 1846. John Hughes, registrar of Bangor, leased the Old Mine in 1846. He was also manager of royalties paid to the Bishop of

Bangor and had Captain Francis as his mine agent at the Old Mine in 1846, and Mr Lester as an under-agent.

A boundary dispute with the Ty'n y Coed Mining Company in 1842 meant that further developments were slow, but by 1846 the Worthingtons had again leased the mine from John Hughes. It was by then a thriving business, and had engines, pumping equipment, a counting house, smithy, small brass foundry, assay office, carpenter's shop, four miners' cabins, two warehouses, a powder house, coal sheds, dressing floor, and ten miners' cottages for families let at £25 a year. Fourteen men were employed in the mine, the highest earner being Captain Davey who earned £200 a year. Joseph Tamblin earned 15/-a week as a pitman and engineer. Two other enginemen earned 12/- a week and the one in charge of the water pressure engine went home with 14/- a week. The other workers' wages ranged from 10/- a week earned by the two labourers, to 15/- a week earned by the underground carpenter. The twenty-two shaft workers, who worked day and night shifts, were paid per yard of ore shifted, and a further fifty-three were paid per quantity of ore raised.

Flooding caused much trouble in 1849 when up to 1,000,000 gallons of water poured into the mine. This resulted in the works being closed for several months. In 1853 8,000 new shares were sold to raise capital of £16,000 for the Llandudno Mine, managed by John Taylor & Sons, and by William Bulkeley Hughes, Member of Parliament for Caernarvon. Robert Vaughan Wynne Williams, Chairman of the Board of the Llandudno Company, invested £5,500 in the venture.

Another problem raised its head when the management found that the workers were working what is now known as 'flexi hours', coming and going as they pleased as long as they worked their allocated six hours per day. Not only did the new company want to change the working pattern, they also wanted to lengthen the daily shift to eight hours. The men went on strike, and held out for seven months until forced back to work in 1855.

Captain David Lloyd was a miner and master mariner who became leaseholder of Old Mine in 1861. He felt he had to invest his money wisely. This he did by building the only ship known to have been built at Llandudno and naming it after Mrs Sarah Lloyd, his wife.

The New Mine (first referred to under that title in 1807) is on Mostyn land near Pyllau, close to the oldest working site on The Orme. It produced good quality ore, which was originally smelted with Anglesey ore in Ravenhead and at the Stanley Works. It was sent to Swansea and Amlwch in 1813 or 1814. Shareholders in the New Mine included John Lloyd of Wigfair; Edward Lloyd of Cefn, St Asaph; George Griffith of Wrexham, and Elizabeth Lester, Tŷ Coch, Llandudno.

Production was high and between 1810 and 1813 Stanley & Co. paid an average of £3,470 per year for New Mine ore. In 1810, Ravenhead of St Helens paid £600 and in 1811 paid £789 for New Mine ore; a dramatic rise was seen by 1812, when Ravenhead paid £3,250 for New Mine ore.

George Edwards was a long-serving mine agent at the New Mine until 1813 when he was eighty-four years old, followed by William Jones from 1813 to 1827. Another to hold the same post was Edward Jones, and the last agent at the New Mine was Thomas Jones.

In June 1815, 165 tons of ore from the mine was sold at Swansea for £2,450. In the next month 112 tons of ore raised a price of £1,608. This level of productivity did not continue and in 1824 only 120 tons had been raised in a quarter. The company, at this time, were also spending money on further developing the mine and sinking shafts. In

1830 they paid £280 for sinking the Pen-y-ffridd Shaft. Continuing work on draining the mine had to be carried out. Twelve miners worked from February 1834 to 17 October 1842, clearing 874 yards. The Penmorfa Level, which stretched from the West Shore to the New Mine and drained flooded workings, was completed on 14 October 1842. A local poet got to work and composed a series of nine *englynion* (Welsh-language poems) about the mine. These were published in the *Carnarvon & Denbigh Herald* on 29 October 1842. Flooding and other problems meant that ore production figures were quite low that year, and caused a great deal of worry for the new owner, Edward Lloyd of Cefn New Mine. The situation did not really improve and only 107 tons were raised in 1861, 125 tons in 1862, and a lowly thirty-nine tons in 1863.

In that year only four men worked the mine. This increased to about a dozen in the winter months when there was less tourist trade work to be found. After 1864 very little work was carried out at the mine.

The beginning of the new century brought some hope to Llandudno's miners, with Charles Horsefield, of Bolton and Glan y Don, Llandudno, obtaining permission in 1911 to prospect and survey the mine. His grand plans, unfortunately, came to nothing.

Possibly the luckiest discovery of ore was made on the site of the Tŷ Gwyn Mine site in 1835. Tŷ Gwyn was one of the twelve original farms of Llandudno. Benjamin Edwards of Plas had two cows which were allowed to graze on Edward Jones' land at Tŷ Gwyn, Y Fach. When one of the cows slipped in the field, in what is now known as the Happy Valley, the turf was dislodged and copper ore was seen underneath the surface.

Edward Jones, quick to realise the beneficial results of

such a discovery, asked permission of the Mostyn Estate (the landowners) to search further. As he was unable to finance the work himself, he sold 124 shares in the venture to a syndicate. The majority shareholder was a local man, William Jones of Bodhyfryd, Llandudno, who purchased twenty-three shares. Another was John Douglas of Gyrn Castle, Flintshire, who bought seventeen shares. Mr Vickers, Joseph Jones, Richard Williams, George Littlewood, William Williamson, Joseph Lyon, E. Jones, Thomas Jones, Edward Hughes and Mr Hove had smaller holdings. Edward Jones kept only two shares for himself.

Two shafts were opened initially, one being the Ty'n y Fron Shaft and the other the Tŷ Gwyn Shaft, followed by Yr Wyddfyd Shaft. John Williams was appointed mine agent and Thomas Owen mine captain. A later captain was George Brookes. A pumping engine from the Halkyn lead mines was installed on 27 August 1837, and another in 1841, to clear the shafts of water. Flooding was a constant problem and more pumps were needed. Buying the engine and installing it in a purpose-built boiler house cost £7,812. Further problems with flooding and the engine breaking down led to the mine being £3,828 in debt by March 1842. Income fell from £5,368 in 1841 to only £187 in 1845. Men were left unpaid.

A further problem was the death in 1839 of John Douglas, one of the major shareholders. His widow was unable to provide any further capital, so his shares were sold for £1,100 in 1846. When all debts had been settled, Mrs Douglas was left with £86 12s 2d. New management took over and William Jones (another major shareholder) and other directors held a party and firework display at a Llandudno hotel in 1846, at which the company's name was changed to Ty'n y Fron Company.

In 1850, the mine was again flooded by the sea. It was

sealed off. The workers walked out. Many of them never returned. By 1853 the shareholders had had enough and decided to close the mine and sell off the equipment. Auctions were held on the site in August 1855 and on 4 July 1856, 'at Twelve for One o'clock prompt'.[2] Mr Wheatley Kirk, of Cross-street Chambers, Manchester and 4 Kirkgate, Leeds, was the auctioneer. Mr Kirk was 'honoured with instructions from the proprietors to sell by auction the WHOLE of the exceedingly valuable PLANT, STEAM-ENGINE, BOILERS &c.'[3] All the mine buildings and engine houses were demolished. Llandudno, by then, had another industry. The growing tourist trade needed hotel rooms, and foundations for a Victorian seaside pier were built. Labour and land were needed for the new ventures, which held more appeal for local workers than the constant struggle in the cold, damp and wet mines and shafts.

In the years it worked, the mine had produced more than £100,000 worth of copper ore – £93,000 worth during the first profitable twelve years. All the mining work that had taken place at Tŷ Gwyn was forgotten about until 1986, when it was rediscovered during more construction work near the pier entrance.

Shaft names are still remembered and noted on Llandudno maps. Some names recall important individuals: Treweek's Shaft and Vivian Shaft (or Copper Ddu, Engine Shaft and the Sump Shaft, to give it its other names), all of which appear on one map or another.

Captain James Treweek (1779–1852) was originally from Gwennap, Cornwall, but moved to Amlwch in 1811. He was mine steward/supervisor on Parys Mountain for thirty-seven years. Amongst his duties was paying 'smoke trespass' to the curate of St Eleth's Church, Amlwch, because the smoke created a nuisance in the curate's house! It was he also, who paid an 'English duty' for having one English church service every Sunday. He became a ship owner and a staunch Wesleyan – and a member of the Welsh Wesleyan congregation after he learnt to speak Welsh. He was an able preacher in both languages and a man who was influential in his work, respected by his master and employees alike, and who mixed freely with the great and the good on the island. He was buried in St Eleth's churchyard.

Treweek knew other Cornishmen who worked at Llandudno and came into regular contact with them, as he was very much in favour of buying Llandudno ore for the Amlwch smelter. He continued to do this from 1829 until his death in 1852.

Captain William Vivian was another of the many Cornishmen who moved to north Wales. He was employed as a mine captain at the Old Mine. 'Captain' was a title given to a mine agent or steward – especially so in Cornwall. He would have been responsible for the day-to-day running of the mine. Two other Cornishmen who moved to Llandudno were Captain George Davey, who was paid £50 per quarter for his work as a mine agent, and James Sims of Redruth, who worked as a mining engineer and engine builder. Thomas Kendrick, a retired copper miner, gave his name to a cave in which he discovered evidence of Neolithic man and animals in 1879.

Other shafts were given descriptive, old Welsh names which were already in use: Cae Llwyn Helyg (*cae*: field; *helyg*: willow), Ffynnon (well) Gogarth, Hafnant Shaft, Pen-y-ffridd (*pen*: head; *ffridd*: mountain pasture) and Pen-y-Gwaith (*gwaith*: work/works). One other name, Bryniau Poethion (*poeth*: hot; *bryniau*: hills), may well be a reminder of the fires that were lit to loosen the ore from the rock or in smelting the ore when they had been brought to the surface. Another name was given to the area after prospectors

Joseph Jones and William Jones of Bodhyfryd discovered copper ore only a yard and a half from the surface on Bryniau Poethion common land. This sparked a 'Welsh California' when all kinds of men came to find their fortune, just as they had gone to the Californian gold rush of 1848 to 1855.

During the working years of all the Llandudno copper mines only two fatal accidents were recorded. Details are few and far between, but Thomas Evans was killed in a mine accident in 1770 and John Davies of Bodafon in 1813. Others, such as John Williams, a sailor and miner, were far more fortunate. He survived a shipwreck on New Year's Day 1824. According to reports he was able to walk ashore and spent the rest of his working life working on the Orme.

Another John Williams began working in the mines at twelve years of age. His father had been there before him and put in a total service of sixty-five years at the mine. Due to his youth and the dangerous condition of the ladders, John's father made him walk an extra three-quarters of a mile overground every day, rather than let him use a short cut to work through underground workings.

Miners worked together in groups. They were known by the name of their leader, who would negotiate terms on his group's behalf for a 'pitch' to work, one of which was known as 'Thomas Lloyd the Bargain'. Some bargains would be easier or better than others and produced more ore, which meant that a good bargain would secure the men more pay; but if the wrong choice of bargain was made, wages would be low.

As Llandudno did not have a smelter of its own, all the ore mined had to be shipped to Amlwch, Lancashire or Swansea, which were the main smelting centres, or anywhere else where the work could be done. Llandudno did not have, and still does not have, a port of its own, not even a proper landing stage, so the ships would be beached on high tide, loaded, and re-floated on the next high tide. Such ships were all from local ports, as there was no history of shipbuilding in Llandudno (apart from the *Mrs Sarah Lloyd*). Dafydd Jones Tŷ Draw was employed in carrying the ore from the mine to the ship; so were Owen Jones (Gogarth) and Thomas Lester. It was usually the same ones who had loaded the ore into the ships on the beach near Glan-y-môr Terrace or from the West Shore who unloaded the coal that was brought back on the return voyages.

Thomas Kendrick was one miner who came to prominence after he left the mines. In short, he was the one who discovered and conclusively proved that Neolithic Man had lived in Llandudno. He was born in 1821 at Pant y Wennol, but after his father's death in 1835 the family had to leave, and moved out of the town. When the family returned to Llandudno to 4 Tan yr Ogof Terrace, Thomas and his brother William found employment in the copper mines.

Thomas built the first camera obscura made of stone in Llandudno and when the mines closed, he realised his ambition to set himself up in business as a lapidarist (one who cuts, polishes, engraves and sells precious and semi-precious stones). His workshop was in what is known today as Kendrick's Cave, with living quarters above the ground floor working area. On enlarging the cave in 1879, he broke through into an inner cavern. Amongst the boulders and rubble he found animal and human bones. These were recognised by palaeontologists as being from the Neolithic period. When measured accurately the bones were identified as the remains of a family: three adults and one child. The adults were over 5 feet 4 inches tall and more than likely members of the Iberic Aborigines who lived in Western Europe, north of the Mediterranean and west of the Rhine. Animal remains included badger, bison, boar, brown bear, horse, red deer, sheep or goat, and short-horned ox. Thomas opened a small museum to display his discoveries – the first museum of any kind in Llandudno. He died on 26 December 1897 of bronchial pneumonia at the age of seventy-six and was buried at St Tudno's church on the last day of that year.

From a sample of 450 names taken from the 1841 Census for the Upper Township of Llandudno, 158 (35 per cent) were listed as copper miners or in work connected with the copper mine. Some were engineers (one of whom was only thirteen years old) or mine agents – William Parry of Tŷ Gwyrdd. Many were father and son combinations, more than likely working the same bargain with the elders looking after the youngsters.

The oldest miner still working was John Jones, Tan y Graig (seventy-five years old); the youngest being Edward Roberts, Tan y Stage, and Eleasar Jones, Cross Onnen, both of whom were only twelve years old.

It would appear that mining was 'young men's work', with 131 of the 158 being younger than fifty years old and only twenty-seven being older than fifty.

From a sample of 437 names taken from the 1851 Census, seventy (16 per cent) worked as miners, with one being classified as a copper ore dresser. The oldest was Richard Lester (seventy-two years old), of Chapel Bach, who, having been born in Amlwch, Anglesey, might well have had previous experience of the same job. The youngest was Isaac Jones (fourteen years old). Of all the workers in the mine, fifty had been born in Llandudno, seven were from other parts of Caernarvonshire, six came from Anglesey, two from Denbighshire, four from Flintshire and one from Liverpool.

The 1861 Census sample of 1,075 names has only twenty-nine miners listed (almost three per cent), including one Miner/Publican. Owen Williams, 9 Back of Mostyn

Street, was the oldest (seventy-two years old), and the youngest was Owen Jones of 8 Wyddfyd Cottage (thirteen years old). Twenty were Llandudno-born and bred; the others came from Conwy, Llanwenllwyfo, Penysarn and Amlwch, Anglesey, Halki(y)n, Holywell and Llanasa in Flintshire.

By 1871 only nine miners were named in a survey of 1,389 names (less than 1 per cent). It was noticeable that many had moved from the Orme to live in the town, grouped together in 12, 13, 14, 15 and 17 Madoc Street; one in Back of Mostyn Street and one in Mostyn Street. Most were elderly workers by now, with seven in the fifty-plus age group and only two young men. Of the nine named, one was the Mine Agent who lived in Canton Villa; seven were Miners and one worked part-time as a Miner/House Colourer. Five were originally from Llandudno, three were from Amlwch, Anglesey, and one had moved into the area from Liverpool.

One ordinary family involved in the mining industry in Llandudno was that of Samuel and Mary Edwards. Their lives can, to some extent, be traced through the Census Returns. Samuel and Mary were Llandudno-born and bred. Samuel was born in 1817; his wife Mary, was five years younger. In 1851, their family consisted of three sons: Owen (seven years old), John (five) and William (three), and their only daughter, 12-month-old Elinor.

Owen was the only scholar listed in the family. Samuel was a miner. He was described as a devout Christian and a member of the Baptist congregation, into which he had been baptised when he was twenty years old. When he saw a particularly striking portrait of the Baptism of Christ, he fell to his knees in prayer and burst into tears. Samuel was also known as a strong and brave swimmer who had saved a number of people from drowning.

By 1861 the growing family had moved to Mona View. Samuel had left the mine to work as a Town Labourer and Owen was old enough to find employment as a House Painter. William and Elinor were the scholars in the family, as was 7-year-old Sarah. New additions were Robert (six years old) and Jane (two years old). John, who would by then have been fifteen years old, is unaccounted for.

When another decade had passed by, the family had moved to 40 Mostyn Street, quite a prestigious address on the main street. Samuel was back in the mine but Mary was now described as a Lodging House Keeper. They had a growing family to keep. Family finances were also boosted by Owen's income from his work as a Joiner, William's as a Plasterer and Sarah's as a Waitress. Elinor is not mentioned as living at home. She could well have married by then. Robert and Jane were still at school, as were Samuel (nine years old) and Hugh (six years old).

Samuel (senior) was sixty-four years old when the census was taken in 1881. Working in the mine was becoming too much hard work. He is listed as a Lodging House Keeper and Mary as a Lodging House Keeper's wife at Bunyan Villa, Chapel Street, Llandudno. Owen and William had flown the nest but Sarah (twenty-nine years old) lived at home working as a Domestic Servant. Robert (twenty-five) worked as a Painter, Samuel Jnr (nineteen) worked as a Plasterer and Hugh (sixteen) worked as a Painter. Mary Ellen, a niece from Samuel's side of the family (nine) lived with them and was a scholar. On the night of the Census, Frank Hughes, a 22-year-old Liverpool Bank Clerk, was also staying as a lodger in Bunyan Villa. The only other occupier was Mary Rees, an unmarried, 25-year-old General Servant, of Machynlleth, Montgomeryshire.

According to the 1891 details, Mary Edwards was a widow but still living at Bunyan Villa. Jane, her unmarried daughter, was living at home and working as a Cook, possibly for her mother in the Lodging House. Mary Ellen, now named as a grand-daughter, was still there earning her living as a Milliner and Dressmaker. Another occupant was Annie Pritchard, a 20-year-old single girl from Port Dinorwic, Caernarvonshire, who was a General Domestic Servant. The only lodger was William Evans, a 42-year-old widower from Llangystenin, Caernarvonshire, who worked as a Joiner.

Next door at Croydon Villa lived Mary's son Hugh and his wife Jane Ellen, of Amlwch, Anglesey. He was still employed as a Painter whilst she was a Lodging House Keeper. Robert (House Painter) and his wife Ann Jones (twenty-eight) were living at Tan yr Ogo' Cottages. Not one member of the family had to earn their living in the copper mines by then, as all three 'modern' mines in Llandudno had closed. The Tŷ Gwyn Mine was the first to close in 1853; the New Mine in 1864 and lastly, the Old Mine in 1881.

By 1881, after a period of twenty-eight years, all 'heavy' industry in the town had disappeared, and the much 'lighter' tourist industry offered many other employment opportunities.

[1] *Lewis Morris – Plans in St George's Channel – 1748*. G. Budenberg (ed.). Lewis Morris Productions, 1967).

[2] *Mining Journal*. 28 June 1856.

[3] *Ibid.*

Anglesey's copper industry

3

Parys Mountain and Anglesey

Anglesey has not been blessed with mountains, but one of its hills ('though denominated a mountain, in Caernarvonshire, at least would be deemed a very inconsiderable hillock'[1]) has a most interesting history. This hill is known locally as Mynydd Parys (*Parys Mountain*), and rises to a height of 482 feet. It was, at one time, a hive of activity due to what can be truly described as a 'boom time' in the copper industry.

Today it has the appearance of a lunar landscape but is, in reality, an industrial heritage site of great importance. During a brief period in the eighteenth and nineteenth century, Parys Mountain was the world's most important copper-producing site. It played a distinctive role in the Industrial Revolution and was a major factor in the global copper economy.

Lewis Morris (1701–1765), hydrographer, lexicographer, poet and antiquary, was not impressed with what he saw at Amlwch or at Amlwch Port in 1748. He saw no purpose in producing a plan of Amlwch Port in his *Plans of Harbours, Bars, Bays and Roads in St George's Channel*, published in September of that year. His description of Amlwch reads:

This is small Creek, two Miles to the West of Elianus's Point, in the North of Anglesey. I did not think it worth while to publish a Plan of this, as it is now, because it is no more than a Cove between two steep Rocks, where a Vessel hath not Room to wind, even at High-water. But a large Vessel might be saved here, in Face of Necessity,

Porth y Rhaw, Pembrokeshire
© *Copyright Richard Law and licensed for reuse under*
Creative Commons Licence

Penpleidiau, Pembrokeshire
© *Copyright David Smith and licensed for reuse under*
Creative Commons Licence

End of the line for the Tennant Canal
© *Copyright Alan Bowring and licensed for reuse under Creative Commons Licence*

Morfa Copper Works (site of)
Copyright vectorkraft and licensed for reuse under Creative Commons Licence

White Rock Works Swansea

Hafod Works Swansea

Sygun Copper Mine, Beddgelert in Snowdonia
© Copyright Gareth James and licensed for reuse under
Creative Commons Licence

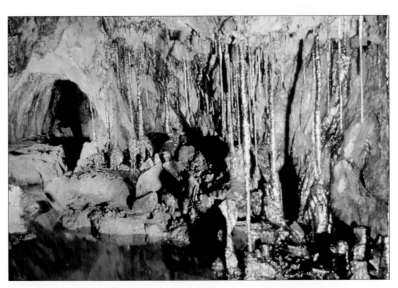

One of the caverns in the Sygun copper mine

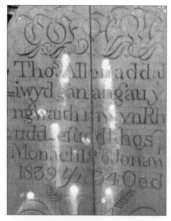

Gravestone of Thos. Allen, 'caught by death' in Rhos Monach Mine, Anglesey on 12 January 1839

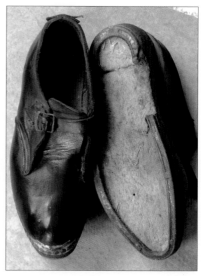

Clogs worn by the Copper Ladies

St Eleth's Church, Amlwch, Anglesey

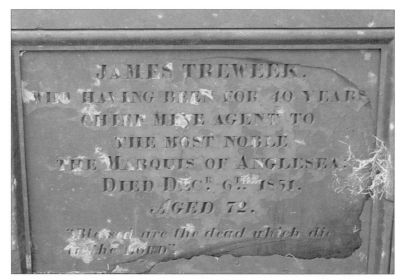

Grave of James Treweek at St Eleth's Church, Amlwch, Anglesey

Remains of Mona Yard on Parys Mountain

Remains of Parys Mountain Windmill

The Great Opencast, Parys Mountain, Anglesey

Slag heaps on Parys Mountain

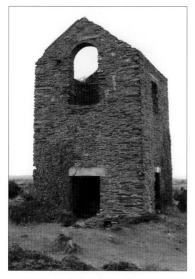

*Pearl Engine House
on Parys Mountain*

*Amlwch Port lighthouse and
watch house*

Amlwch Port quay side with restored copper storage bin

The Old Quay and Far Side Ship Yard at Amlwch Port

Precipitation Pits on Parys Mountain

*Morris Shaft and Graig Wen on Morfa Du site,
Parys Mountain*

Entrance to Llandudno Copper Mine

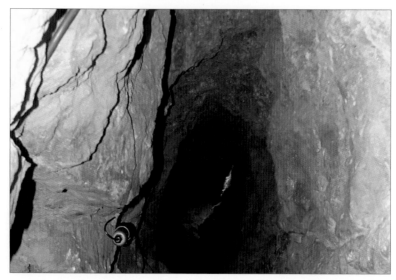

Narrow underground passage at Llandudno Copper Mine

Concealed (almost) entrance to shaft, Llandudno Copper Mine

Stone hammers and knock stones at Llandudno Copper Mine

Underground cavern entrance at Llandudno Copper Mine

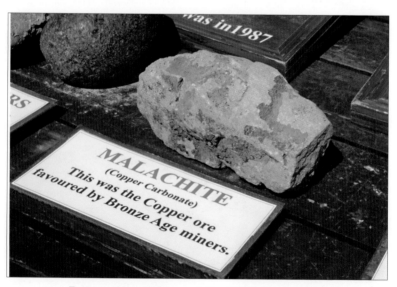

Bronze Age evidence at the Great Orme mine

Victorian copper mining displayed at Llandudno Museum

Prehistoric tunnels excavated under the old Victorian rubble

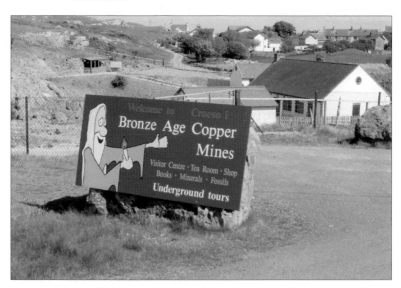

The Heritage Centre at the Great Orme mine

Basingwerk Abbey, Flintshire

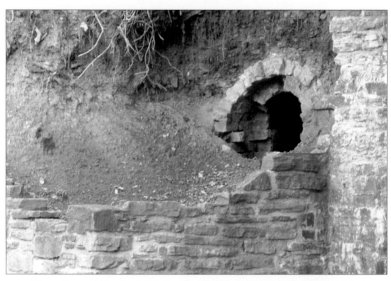

Remains of Greenfield Copper Mills, Greenfield, Flintshire

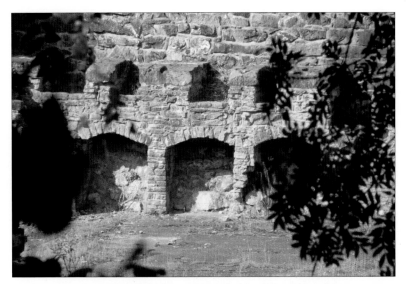

Industrial remains at Greenfield Mills, Flintshire

Remains of Meadow Mill, Greenfield, Flintshire

*Culverts supplying water from lake to Meadow Mill,
Greenfield, Flintshire*

Industrial remains at Meadow Mill, Greenfield, Flintshire

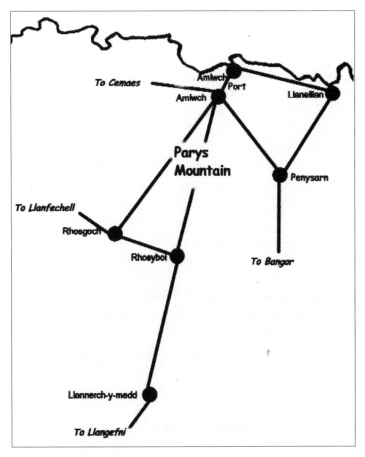

*Sketch map of the Amlwch and Parys Mountain
area in Anglesey*

provided the Mouth of the Harbour can be discovered,
which is now difficult for a stranger.

IMPROVEMENTS: Two White Houses, for Land-
marks, one on each Side the Harbour's Mouth, would
make the Entrance conspicuous to any Stranger; the
Eastern-most Mouse, a small island near the place, being
a good Direction till you come close to the Shore.

By the time Reverend J. Skinner visited Amlwch in December 1802, it had grown significantly to:

> a long straggling place and may contain from four to five thousand inhabitants. Besides two or three good houses a church has lately been erected by the copper company.

But information supplied by S. Dew for the 1847 *Report of the Education Commissioners* contained some depressing facts. Amlwch's population had grown to 6,217, the majority of whom either worked in the copper mines or in the harbour. Many of the town's children had not had the benefit of educational instruction in either a daily or Sunday school. The Revd W. Roberts, a Methodist minister, added:

> I think there is not a place in the country where there are so many children uneducated. Young children of about seven or eight are able to earn a little in the iron pits, and great numbers of them are employed to pick copper.

And Samuel Greathead, bank manager, added:

> There are few parishes in North Wales in which there is so much real destitution.

Parys Mountain is situated in the north-eastern corner of Anglesey, north Wales, in the parish of Amlwch. The actual site is roughly 1¼ miles long by almost 1 mile wide. Surrounded as it is today by green fields and farms, it is difficult to recognise it for what it once was – a leading industrial site. The multi-coloured rocks, lifeless pools of water and an absence of plants and animals suggest a forlorn place, but it is a place with a history that needs to be told.

The ores worked at Parys Mountain were complex

mixtures of minerals, but two types predominated: the 'yellow ore' and the 'blue ore'. Yellow ore consisted mostly of the brass-coloured copper iron sulphide chalcopyrite, mixed with the iron sulphide, pyrite, and quartz. It was the historically important ore: the blue ore, a mixture of the dark brown zinc sulphide, sphalerite and the bluish-grey lead sulphide, galena, was regarded as waste – although ironically it has been the key focus in recent mineral exploration. Many other minor metallic minerals are now known to be present, including compounds of arsenic, antimony, bismuth, silver and gold. The ores are now understood to have been deposited from solutions emerging from vents in the ancient sea-floor during the late Ordovician and early Silurian periods, some 460–430 million years ago, in association with volcanic activity. They formed as metal-rich sediments.

Weathering of the pyrite by rainwater percolating down through the rocks formed sulphuric acid which then leached other ore minerals and led to the impressive, vivid reddening and yellowing of the rocks in the vicinity. The massive bluestone ore was converted in the near-surface environment into brown, porous masses known as gossan: in the highly acidic environment the lead was redeposited within the gossan as the sulphate. Present in considerable quantities at one time, it was noticed but attempts to produce lead from it met with technical problems. However, its chemistry was worked out and it was described as a mineral in the nineteenth century: it was named Anglesite, after the island of Anglesey.

During the Bronze Age, Parys Mountain was a prehistoric industrial site. Primitive stone hammers have been discovered underground and carbon found with them was carbon-dated by the British Museum to 3500 BC. These stones are not usually found on the mountain but are plentiful on local beaches. This implies that they were carried to the site with a specific purpose in mind. Oak-charcoal has also been found and carbon-dated to 1690 BC–2040 BC. Such material would have been used to smelt the ore from surrounding rocks. Permission has been granted by the local landowner, the Marquis of Anglesey, for further exploration in the hope of finding more prehistoric evidence, but it has to be faced that such evidence has probably disappeared under the eighteenth- and nineteenth-century works.

The Roman Empire, which had spread as far north-west as Anglesey by AD 61, had need of metals found in Britain, including copper. No direct evidence of Roman copper mining from that period has been found on Parys Mountain, but copper ingots, some with distinctive Roman marks have been found on other Anglesey sites which are close to the mountain. This suggests that mining did indeed take place. Two copper 'cakes', weighing 25/30 lbs and marked with the letters 'IVFS', were found on nearby Trysglwyn Farm land, and it is believed that the small fort built at Holyhead was intended to protect the copper mines of Parys Mountain. In the Sail Loft Visitor Centre at Amlwch Port is a copper bun ingot dating back to the time of the Roman occupation of Wales. The ingot was presented to the Amlwch Heritage Trust by a descendent of Thomas Fanning Evans (1841–1891), of Mona Lodge, Amlwch, an ex-Government mine inspector and owner of the Parys Mine Company.

After the Romans left Anglesey and withdrew from Britain, the copper works were more or less forgotten. Very little is known about the site until a change of name at the beginning of the fifteenth century. The original name, Mynydd Trysglwyn (found in at least two local farms) means an area of rough, lichen-covered bushes or trees; the new name came into being with the land's new owner.

In 1406, Robert Parys was granted the land on his appointment as King's Commissioner (or Tax Collector) following Owain Glyn Dŵr's revolt against Henry IV. Glyn Dŵr had extra strong support on Anglesey due to family connections. It was his cousins Gwilym and Rhys ap Tudur that captured and held Conwy castle for two months, and it was from Anglesey that an attack was launched on Caernarfon. All 2,121 supporters of the rebellion from Anglesey were fined.

It is thought that Parys was given the position due to the influence of his mother Siwan or Joan and her second husband, Gwilym ap Gruffydd, of Penrhyn, Llandegai, Gwynedd, who was a staunch supporter of the king. The land passed to Parys' wife on his death and to William Gruffydd Fychan, her son from her second marriage, on her death. In time it was bequeathed to the family of Plas Newydd, Llanfairpwll.

Very little work was carried out on the mountain until the Tudor period, when the demand for copper increased, especially so at a time of war. Henry VIII and his daughter Elizabeth I tried to halt the expensive task of importing copper from Europe, and hoped to find a supply much nearer home.

In 1579, a Mr Medley was present on the mountain conducting an experiment witnessed by Sir John Wynn of Gwydir, who wrote a letter about what he saw to Lord Eure: 'I sende you the mineral water of Anglesey to be tried. I saw Medley made the trial, before Sir Henry Sydney and I laid down the particulars.'[2] Sir John described how a quantity of ore was beaten into a powder and boiled in water in lead containers. When cooled, a layer of 'copperas', 'alome' and 'earth of iron'[3] had formed. Unfortunately, the work would not quitte coste; and so it proved, for that in a while it was given over.'[4] Such was the effect of this experiment that Sir

John still remembered it when he wrote again to Ralph, 3rd Baron Eure, twenty-eight years later, to remind him of what he had seen.

Amlwch (the parish of Saint Eleth) extends to about 9,000 acres of land. In the eighteenth century, almost half belonged to two influential Anglesey families – the Baylys of Plas Newydd, Llanfairpwll, and the Hughes family of Llys Dulas, Llanwenllwyfo.

Sir Nicholas Bayly of Plas Newydd owned about 3,000 acres (Cerrig y Bleiddiau on the eastern side of the mountain), together with another 500 acres (Parys Farm on the western side of the mountain), jointly owned with William Lewis of Llys Dulas. Lewis owned another 800 acres in his own name. Neither of them was aware of the real value of the land and what wealth lay beneath its surface, so neither bothered about the fact that a clearly-defined border between their holdings did not exist. In 1753, Bayly leased Lewis' share of Parys Farm for £25 per annum.

Lewis died in April 1761. On the night before his death he drew out a will which disinherited his niece Mary Lewis, but he died before he could sign the document. His estates were left to Elizabeth, his wife, who, in turn, left all her property to Mary. She and her husband, Reverend Edward Hughes of Lleiniog, Beaumaris, became the owners of the Llys Dulas estate on the death of Elizabeth Lewis in 1770.

In 1760 Dr John Rutty was heard lecturing the Royal Society in London about the waters of Parys Mountain. He recommended them as 'a powerfull detergent, repelling, bracing, styptic, cicatrizing, anti-scorbutic and deobstrument medicine' to help cure ulcers, dysentery, diarrhoea, worms, dropsy, yellow fever and other illnesses.

The Morris brothers, of Pentre-eiriannell on Anglesey, inveterate letter-writers and observers of life, were well aware of what could be found, and what was happening on the mountain and in mining in general, on Anglesey and beyond. William wrote to his brother Lewis on Sunday night, 28 June 1761, to say that mining had started at Rhos Manach. In another letter dated 2 July 1761 he states that their old *cydnabod* (acquaintance) Alex Fraser, Lord Loveld, was working as hard as possible there and in another, later, paragraph he describes how their brother John had ridden over Parys Mountain and that his horse had fallen into a hole that was 6 yards deep and that he (John) also saw copper there.

James Thomas of Cornwall examined the mountain in detail in 1761 and discovered a plentiful supply of ore which he sent to Warrington to be smelted, but his hoped-for fortune failed to materialize.

Henry Rowlands pleaded for the county gentry to co-operate in a search for the mountain's riches, as he was of the opinion that a fortune could be made 'if dexterously sought for'. No one listened. No one realised his dream.

Two men are given credit for rediscovering copper on the mountain. One is Alexander Frazer. Little is known of this Scottish exile but it is believed that he was born about 1663 and was educated at the King's College, Aberdeen, between 1678 and 1683. According to one story he was forced to flee after killing a musician at a dance in 1692. He is credited with discovering copper ore at Cerrig y Bleiddiau, but was forced to abandon his attempts as the workings became flooded. He is remembered as one of the shadier characters who worked at Parys Mountain.

The other is a local miner named Rowland Puw. He is credited as being the discoverer of the Golden Venture, a very rich vein of copper ore, on 2 March 1768. He was much better rewarded than Frazer, with a bottle of brandy and a rent-free cottage for himself and his wife until their deaths in 1786 and 1796. The first shaft dug on the mountain was 80 yards deep, and was named the Golden Venture Shaft.

Almost a hundred years later the uncertainty still existed as to which of the two men was the true rediscoverer – though Puw was given more credit than Frazer, perhaps because he was a local man.

At a local eisteddfod held at Bozrah Chapel, Penysarn, the poet Glan Alaw won with his song of praise to 'Alexander Frazer, founder of the copper ore on Parys Mountain'. His opening lines were:

Hen lol 'di rhoi'r clod i Roland Puw
Choeliwn i mo hynny yn fy myw.[5]

[It is a lot of nonsense to praise Roland Puw,
For the life of me, I can't believe that his story is true.]

It must be remembered that the eisteddfod prize of two guineas was provided by John Fraser of Caernarfon, one of Alexander's descendants!

The first leaseholders of the mountain were Messrs Roe & Co. of Macclesfield, but they were on the point of giving up when Rowland Puw made his discovery in 1768. Shafts were dug – the first ones, by Roe & Co. – to get at the ore. So many, in fact, that the mountainside collapsed, forming a huge pit measuring 200 yards long by 150 yards wide, and between 20 and 40 yards deep. This was known as the 'Great Opencast'. At about this time Tregarnedd, the old home of Ednyfed Fychan, friend and seneschal (steward) of Llywelyn the Great, and ancestor of the Tudor family, became the first Anglesey house to be roofed with copper.

In 1778 the Admiralty realised the benefit of copper-sheathing their ships. Having sheathed or copper-bottomed ships meant that the danger of the shipworm (*Toredo navalis*) was eradicated. Unprotected ships that sailed in warmer waters, and that were attacked by the wood-boring mollusc (finger-thick and an arm's length) had a very uncertain future and had to face costly repairs in dry dock. Protected ships were faster and had a much longer life-span, as any bottom growth of weeds and barnacles could be scraped off.

Copper sheathing was almost abandoned in 1782 as the sheets were held in place by iron bolts. The copper sheets and iron bolts reacted to one another and as the bolts rusted, the sheets loosened, and the exposed timbers were again attacked by the shipworm and rotted. This led to the sinking of the warship *Royal George* in Plymouth Harbour with the loss of 900 men.

New copper bolts were made by Thomas Williams' companies, which meant that he secured work to produce 40,000 bolts per week in 1784. (There is more about Thomas Williams in the next chapters.) Williams also secured contracts from other European navies, a very profitable deal, since each ship required at least 11 tons of copper sheaths, a ton of nails and 20 tons of bolts, all of which would be replaced every four years. Thomas Williams' companies sheathed up to 105 ships per year in Liverpool, and he himself was the owner of forty ore-carrying ships from Amlwch to Holywell and Liverpool, together with contracts for the merchant fleets and from other companies that sailed their ships to Africa and the West Indies: no wonder his business was booming.

In the years between 1768 and 1800, a profit of £193,943 19s. was made by the Mona Mine Company, whilst the Parys Mine Company made £111,693 15s. But problems had to be faced. By 1805 the first period of glory was gradually coming to an end. The Mona Mine Company was wound up in 1811 and a new Mona Mine Company was set up by the second Lord Uxbridge, who later became the first Marquis of Anglesey after his exploits at Waterloo. The aforementioned James Treweek was appointed mine manager. Shafts were driven into the mountainside but suffered the constant problem of flooding, and Cornish beam engines were needed to pump the mines clear of water. The first of its type was placed in the Pearl Engine House in 1819. Others were placed at the Carreg y Doll, Parys Opencast, Cairns, Hillside and Gwen shafts. The mine was busy once more as the price of copper ore had increased by 50 per cent, ranging from £3 2s 6d. to £16 6s. per ton, depending on how much copper was contained in the ore. Pure copper was priced at £140 per ton.

Production rose. In 1829, 16,400 tons of copper ore were raised from the mountain. New shafts were dug, including the Coronation Shaft, which was opened on George IV's coronation day on 19 July 1821. On that day blasting continued from sunrise until eleven o'clock at night. Such a day was the perfect excuse for eating and drinking, and even though two of the men were injured in an explosion, the carousing continued amongst the workers and owners. The Union flag flew above the mine and everybody went home with the sound of 'God Save the King' still ringing in their ears. The village inn at Penysarn was renamed 'The George IV', and it was there that one of my great-uncles celebrated his luck in finding work at the Hills Chemical Works (an off-shoot of the copper works on Parys Mountain) in Amlwch Port. For his labours he received an allowance of a pint of beer for every cartload of artificial fertiliser he carried from the works. It is part of family lore that he drank eight pints a night! A similar celebration was held on the coronation of William IV in 1831.

The population of Amlwch gradually increased, but while the town was growing in size, social problems were also coming to the fore. The Reverend William Roberts, in 1847, described Amlwch as the poorest and most immoral place in Anglesey. Another ten years of real prosperity was to come, with workers earning good wages. Such a situation continued until 1870 when Messrs John Taylor & Sons, the leaseholders, made a £400,000 profit, but problems were beginning to appear. Two mine supervisors left – Captain Trevithick and James Williams – Williams to manage a mine in Canada. By 1874 production was down to only 5,665 tons of ore. The Parys Mine Company's balance sheet for 1879 showed an income of £2,000 but expenses of £4,000. One of the expenses was the cost of installing a windmill to pump water out of the mine. This, a typical Anglesey-type mill (conical shape) but with five rather than the usual four sails, is still standing on the mountain top. Another company took over in 1880, led by local men Thomas Fanning Evans and J. Gwynne Paynter, but suffered problems almost immediately. An American furnace, especially bought for the works, failed and ore which contained far too little copper became solidified inside. The numbers of the employed fell sharply. In 1892 a mere thirty-one miners were working underground, 126 on the surface and only thirty-four at the ochre pits. Things went from bad to worse and by 1901 only the precipitation pits were worth working. This was the end of an era.

There are many sites on Anglesey apart from Parys Mountain where copper ores have been found. They range from inland places to the rocky coast. What they all had in common was that no one made a great deal of money on any of them. These are just a few of the projects that came to nothing, or very little.

In 1623 copper ore was found at Llanddona and Sir John Wynn of Gwydir knew of the site. On 15 September 1756 a twenty-one year lease was granted to John Champion of Holywell by Francis Lloyd, an Anglesey doctor, to mine for copper, tin, calamine and zinc on land at Y Gader on Carmel Head. He would try his hand at the Dolawen mine in Nant Ffrancon in 1760 but failed as he was unable to get on with his partners. A small mine at Rhosymynach, Llanwenllwyfo, was opened in 1827, where low-grade copper ore was mined. In the five years up to 1832, 144 tons of ore was mined there, producing ten tons of copper to the value of £746.

In 1835 the Anglesey Mining Company was keen to mine at Rhosymynach at Llanwenllwyfo. They offered £4,500 but were refused permission when the mine was sold at a higher price to an English company, which failed to make it pay.

Edmund Spargo, who would later become involved with the Snowdon/Britannia Mine, was hard at work at Mynachdy on Garn Mountain, Anglesey in 1863. He was also a lease-holder for the mines at Rhosymynach and at Carmel Head.

On 16 March 1872 a twenty-one year lease was granted to Mr Gibson of London by Mr Pritchard of Trescawen, Capel Coch, to prospect at Pant y Gaseg. Gibson clearly knew very little about Anglesey and its linguistic background, and he had the temerity to ask the miners 'to learn and cultivate a knowledge of English' for his benefit! At the time, only a few of the local population were bilingual, and most spoke only Welsh. His company was dissolved in 1879.

The Pant-y-gaseg Copper Mining Company issued forty shares at £250 pounds each in 1872 but the company was dissolved seven years later in 1879. Another company called the New Cambrian Syndicate worked the mine from 1906 to 1907.

The Rhosymynach mine was reopened in 1917 when the mine reached a depth of 100 feet. Only eighty tons of ore in output was recorded for that year. It was abandoned in 1926.

An old Welsh verse says that if you live frugally, one sheep will eventually become a flock of 2,000; on the other hand, if you live lavishly, they will soon disappear and you'll be left with only one again. The verse could well have been written for those who invested their money in copper mining ventures. Due to the unqualified success of the ventures on Parys Mountain, many thought that they could make the same kind of money elsewhere. Unfortunately, however, this turned out not to be the case.

Parys Mountain had its ups and downs, too, but there were factors that made it a long-term success and other mines short-term failures. One was the men – their drive and inventiveness. Then there were the rich veins of copper and the plentiful supply. A third was the connections made in the right way and at the right times, for instance with shipping and ship-building.

Would the lesser schemes have succeeded if they'd had abler men in charge, with as many resources to deploy? Would less able men have succeeded with richer veins of ore? Would the most able men and the rich veins have succeeded without the parallel development of the connecting infrastructures? There is a big difference between imitation with hope, and innovation with enterprise.

Amlwch and the Port still survive, despite the many ups and downs. Today many of the signs of the nineteenth-century copper industry and ship-building, both responsible for the town's growth, have disappeared. In the 1844 Slaters Business Directory for Amlwch, Morgan and Jones are first mentioned as tobacco manufacturers who, like others, produced cigarettes, snuff, pipe and chewing tobacco from British Empire tobacco leaves imported to Liverpool. By 1985, other brands, by much larger producers, had taken over completely. There was a local brewing industry in the town. The Octel Chemical plant, built in 1953, extracting bromine from sea water for use in petrol engines, was closed in 2004. Even now, signs of the twentieth-century oil industry – a nine days' wonder – have gone from view. A nearby nuclear power station at Wylfa, Cemaes, is soon to close, and unless a new one, known as Wylfa B, is built, the local economy will suffer even further. Amlwch has returned to more days of peace and quiet – until its next awakening.

---

[1] *Ten Days Through the Isle of Anglesea*. Rev. John Skinner. December 1802.
[2] *General View of the Agriculture and Domestic Economy of North Wales*, Volume III. Walter Davies. Sherwood, Neely & Jone, 1810.
[3] *Ibid.*
[4] *Ibid.*
[5] *Mynydd Parys*. Owen Griffith. Cwmni'r Wasg Genedlaethol Cymreig, Caernarfon, 1897.

4

Copper smelting

Put simply, copper smelting is the burning or roasting off of sulphur and other impurities from copper ore to obtain pure copper. If only it *were* that simple! It is a process that involves a great deal of heat and time in the different stages to ensure the process is completed safely and the extraction of the ore is successful.

On Parys Mountain a fairly primitive method was used, and really it was a process which had evolved very little from the Bronze Age. If it wasn't for a German visitor who spent months on Anglesey and wrote of his experiences in letters to a friend back home, very little would be known of how it was done. Augustin Gottfried Ludwig Lentin (1764–1823) was a German chemist. In his early career he was a lecturer at the University of Göttingen, but later he became an inspector of salt mines, and a writer and translator of works on chemistry and metallurgy. Between 1795 and 1801 he visited Wales and spent some months in Amlwch studying the copper works at Parys Mountain, and also the copper works at Ravenhead and Stanley, near St Helens, Lancashire, where copper ore from Parys Mountain was smelted. Lentin was very observant and wrote descriptive letters which were published in Germany in 1800 entitled *Briefe uber die Insel Anglesea.*

His letters contain details of all aspects of the work on Parys Mountain: the companies involved, and the development of Amlwch from a small agricultural and fishing village to a large industrial town. He was also very critical of the way the mountain was mined, and said to his friend that the only reason he included his critical

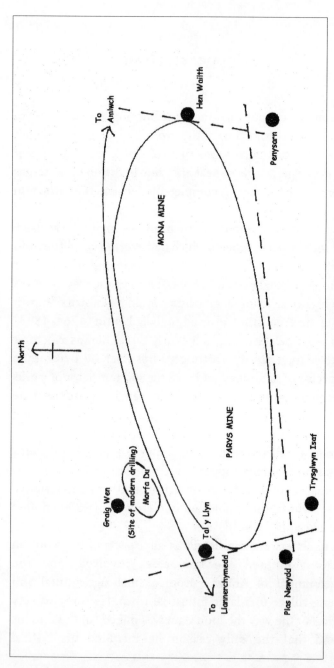

Sketch map of Parys Mountain and its boundaries

description of the works was so that others would learn how not to do it! Some of his not-so-critical comments are about Thomas Williams, and also about the period from 1850 onwards when Anglesey overtook Cornwall as a world leader in the copper trade.

After describing in great detail the Copper Ladies, the team of local women who worked on Mynydd Parys, and their work in breaking down the ores into more manageable lumps, he goes on to explain that the ores were then roasted to rid them of the sulphur content. He gave Thomas Williams due respect for his efforts in building thirty-one furnaces and employing almost a hunded men.

Two kinds of roasters or smelters were used in Amlwch, both of which had been designed by Williams. The first used was a rectangular shape, 70 feet x 20 feet x 8 feet, built of plain stones and clay. The inside walls were straight but the outside was shaped and sloped to look like an oblong pyramid. The roaster had four air vents and was fired by coal. From the roaster, a brick channel was built to connect it to a condenser 60 feet x 8 feet x 6 feet in which was collected sulphuric acid vapour. Coal had to be imported to Amlwch, and thus roasting proved to be an expensive method and with the smelters demanding high wages another method had to be found. Williams petitioned Parliament on four different occasions to ask for the duty paid on coal carried overseas to be lifted. In 1786 a Bill went through Parliament leading to 'An Act for allowing a drawback on duties upon coal used in smelting copper and lead ores and in fire engines for drawing water out of the copper and lead mines within the Isle of Anglesey'.[1]

Williams' second type of smelter was a conical furnace with an 8 feet high, brick-built base. The cone on top of the base was 27 feet high, with 2 feet thick walls, 16 feet wide at the bottom in which were located four 2-feet square draught holes 4 feet wide on the inside at the top, so scrapers could be used to reach the inside of the furnace. This stone structure was supported on the inside by reinforced iron rods. At the top was a 2-foot square hole, covered with an iron plate, through which the ore was thrown in. A condenser was connected to the furnace as well. So efficient and effective did they prove to be that by 1786 forty-five of them were built in Amlwch Port. The process of smelting and final refining of copper ore was not completed at Amlwch Port and partially smelted/roasted ore was sent in 80–300 ton ships to Liverpool, unloaded into barges and sent along the Liverpool-Wigan-Leeds Canal to the Ravenhead and Stanley Works.

These methods of smelting were further developed at Swansea until smelting by 'The Welsh Process' became an accepted practice.

Stage 1 **Calcination**

This first stage is the one that rids the ore of most of the sulphur and other impurities, such as arsenic. Between three and five tons of ore were roasted (not burned) whilst the temperature was gradually raised to 800 degrees Celsius. The ore had to be stirred to make sure that it was all heated up to the same temperature and did not coagulate in a semi-molten state. By keeping the temperature at a constant 800 degrees Celsius for between 12 and 24 hours, the sulphur would turn to vapour and the copper did not melt. At the end of the stage the ore was put in chambers below the furnace where it was cooled with cold water. Calcining took place on the mountainside, and produced acrid smoke.

Stage 2 **Melting**

Calcined ore was transferred to another furnace and melted using slag produced in Stage 4 as a flux to promote the fusion of the metal. The furnace had to be completely sealed, and a temperature of 1,150 degrees Celsius maintained for 5 hours to melt the ore. After raking, the slag, into which the iron oxides present in the calcined ore would have been to an extent partitioned, would be taken off by skimming the surface of the melted ore. This process would be repeated until the furnace bottom would be full of molten regulus which contained up to 35 per cent pure copper, 35 per cent iron and 30 per cent sulphur. When the furnace was opened or 'tapped', the molten regulus would flow out into cold water in which it would turn to granules. The slag would then be discarded as waste material.

Stage 3 **Re-calcination**

At this stage 2 tons of the hardened granules of regulus were roasted for 24 hours. During this time it would be stirred and opened to air. The amount of sulphur in the regulus would be further reduced to 15 per cent.

Stage 4 **Mixing**

What was left after Stage 3 was mixed with other ores containing carbonates, oxides of copper and slag from Stages 5 and 6. The mixture was melted at 1,200 degrees Celsius in a metal furnace and the slag skimmed off for further use. By the end of the stage the mixture would be 75 per cent copper. It was let out into sand moulds and left to cool.

Stage 5 **Roasting and Melting**

The metal was cooled in the moulds. When the

moulds were turned out the lumps of metal were known as Cast Pigs. These were roasted and melted for another 8 hours. During this time air would be allowed in the furnace to make sure that any remaining sulphur was burnt off. The metal was heated and cooled more than once to ensure that all the sulphur dioxide (SO_2) had been dispersed. The mixture was also skimmed and the slag taken out and be prepared as a flux for Stage 4. When let out of the furnace the 95 per cent pure copper was again run into sand moulds and left to cool to become what was known as Blistered Copper.

Stage 6   **Refining**

This was the final stage of a very laborious process in which the furnace was loaded with between 6 and 8 tons of blistered copper, which were then melted for up to 24 hours. Air was let in to help the firing. Slag was taken off and the molten metal tested for purity and to see if it could be called 'refined copper'. To rid the molten copper of any gas that may have accumulated, anthracite was put on the surface and branches of green birch or oak were thrown in. The wood and coal would cause the gases to escape. By this stage the molten copper was known as 'tough pitch' or 'cake' copper and ladled into moulds or into a bath of cold water to make 'feathered-out copper'. A depression in the surface of the copper meant that it had been affected by too much oxygen. A ridge indicated the presence of too much gas, mainly hydrogen. Satisfactory 'tough pitch' copper had a wrinkled surface and could be bent double after hammering and had a silky fracture.

Most of the slag that was produced during the smelting process was re-used in Stage 2, but some was turned into a building material known as Scoria, easily recognised by its shiny, glass-resembling vitreous surface.

One problem resulting from smelting was the waste sulphur dioxide which was produced. When it was released into the atmosphere, it mixed with water vapour or rain and became sulphuric acid (H_2SO_4) (or what is known today as acid rain), which was, and is, harmful to many life forms.

---

[1] Copper Mountain. John Rowlands, Anglesey Antiquarian Society, 1981.

5

Movers and shakers

'Movers and shakers' are people of an energetic demeanour who initiate change and influence events. Many such people worked in the copper mines on Parys Mountain, and without their efforts the place would never have become the world leader and biggest influence on the copper market of its time. Their influence on the works and town of Amlwch was phenomenal. Amlwch, in its heyday, developed from a small hamlet of about half a dozen houses to one of the biggest towns in Wales. Surrounding villages grew and developed. Fortunes were made – and some were lost. Parys Mountain drew the world's attention to Anglesey and gave it an economic foundation on which to build for the future. Sadly those days are gone, but the contribution of these original 'movers and shakers' cannot be ignored.

It would be easy to describe Thomas Williams simply as an industrialist, but to do so would be a great disservice to his memory for he was much, much more. He should be considered as the greatest of the movers and shakers who were involved in the industrial history of Parys Mountain.

Titles are a reflection on a man's standing within his community. To gain the title of 'Copper King' meant that the person in question, loved or hated, was very important and influential, and had certain qualities that were apparent and recognised by his peers. To have been elevated to the status of Copper King, Thomas Williams would have had to have had advanced technical skills and the ability to transfer them; excellent financial foresight and acumen; a wide sphere of interests, both inside and outside the copper industries; would have been good at promoting himself and his projects, successful in his understanding of human relationships, and in possession of political skills. That he had such attributes is not in doubt and the fact that his peers admitted to this, even if sometimes grudgingly, was a mark of his abilities and greatness.

Thomas Williams and his story are synonymous with that of Parys Mountain. Thanks to Williams' business acumen, the copper mines of Parys Mountain came to the forefront of the dramatic events of world copper production between 1768 and 1810.

Many descriptions, some rather insulting and others complimentary, have been given to Thomas Williams. He was known as being remarkable for quick decisions and ruthless action when his business interests were at stake. His business rival Matthew Boulton described him as 'the despotick sovereign of the copper trade',[1] and advised others to be 'extremely cautious in your dealings with Williams'.[2] James Watt went even further and spoke of him as 'a perfect tyrant and not over tenacious of his word and will screw damned hard when he has got anybody in his vice.'[3] Such descriptions were not the best of character references for anyone, but Williams was not just 'anyone'. He was as important an industrial pioneer as any other during the Industrial Revolution in Wales, and his influence on the home and world copper market was such that Pascoe Grenfell, a Swansea industrialist, said, 'Take him all in all, it is hardly to be expected that we shall meet his like again'.[4]

Like many other truly great men, Thomas Williams was a very complex character – even an enigma, according to John Rowlands. He became a man of great wealth who donated generously to the Amlwch poor and towards the rebuilding of the town church. The Amlwch Church Vestry Book for 1794 has the minute:

It was resolved unanimously that the thanks of the Vestry in the name of the Parish be conveyed to Thomas Williams, Esq., for the liberal donation towards rebuilding or repairing the Church. As a noble instance of magnanimity under much misrepresentation, it was resolved that a letter addressed to the Church Wardens by Thomas Williams, Esq., be read and deposited among the most valuable of the parish records.[5]

At the same time, the Bishop of Bangor thought of him as one who was fleecing the area in order to line his own pockets! Because of his many charitable acts, which benefitted so many of his workers, he was known to the Anglesey working classes as *Twm Chwarae Teg* (Tom Fair Play), and it is by this name that he is still remembered today. (He had another colloquial name – *Shôn Gwialan* – under which name he may well have produced, if not written, a pamphlet condemning Bishop Warren of Bangor – who was also the vicar of Amlwch, but had resisted plans to build the new church.)

Thomas Williams was a Welsh-speaker from Anglesey, born on 13 May 1737. He became a respected county lawyer who rose to represent the Llys Dulas family in a dispute about Parys Mountain boundaries. Eventually, he was one of the pioneers of the Industrial Revolution, and was a hero to the Anglesey working classes, even though he represented Great Marlow, Buckinghamshire as Member of Parliament from 1790 to 1802. His Temple Mills Copper Works was also sited there. He was works manager for both Nicholas Bayly and the Reverend Edward Hughes.

Williams was an extremely hard worker who looked after his own interests as well as his employers'. As a leading county lawyer he certainly dealt with land issues etc, but the issue which brought him in contact with the copper industry was the dispute between the Llys Dulas and Plas Newydd families regarding boundaries to their land on Parys Mountain. He was appointed lawyer to the Llys Dulas family and the dispute lasted long enough for him to gain a valuable insight into industrial matters. With the information he had gleaned he decided to join with the Reverend Edward Hughes to form a company to mine the western side of the mountain. With the assistance of John Dawes, a London banker, who in 1778 arranged a lease for the Parys Farm site on Parys Mountain, the three set up the Parys Mine Company.

In 1785, when a lease on the eastern side of Parys Mountain held by Roe & Co. of Macclesfield expired, Nicholas Bayly of Plas Newydd decided not to renew it. He set up his own mining company and invited his old legal adversary, Thomas Williams, to join with him. Williams had shown his rivals that he was more than capable of running a very successful company and for the rivals it was a case of 'better the Devil you know'. The Mona Mine Company was formed with Bayly and Williams as partners. At the time the two companies were responsible for the production of a third of British copper ore. Up to 1,200 people worked for the companies. To pay their wages, Thomas Williams decided to mint his own copper tokens payable in London, Liverpool and Anglesey.

Williams also set up a partnership with John Westwood of Birmingham, who owned the rights to a copper-rolling mill for producing copper sheaths to protect ships' bottoms. He sold the copper sheaths to the Admiralty. In 1785 together with Matthew Boulton, John Wilkinson and Henry Vivian he established the Cornish Metal Company to sell copper from Anglesey and Cornwall. His powers seemed to be absolute. As a letter from the chief agent, Thomas Harrison, to his master Lord Uxbridge, of Plas Newydd,

Llanfairpwll, states 'that every ounce of Copper produced by Cornwall is to *be sold by Mr Williams for five years* and no other Man upon Earth is to sell an atom of it'.[6] Williams was shrewd enough to ensure that a percentage of the Anglesey copper was not sold under the company's name but was held back to be sold in his own name for a more reasonable price, thus ensuring a sure sale and more profit for himself.

Thomas Williams built copper smelting plants to compete with Swansea and also invested in the Cornish tin industry. In his years connected with Parys Mountain, it has been estimated that 130,000 tons of ore were mined from the mountain. Some said he was responsible for over-producing. However, with the control that he exercised over all aspects of the industry with his smelters in Amlwch, Ravenhead, Stanley and Swansea; rolling mills in Holywell and the Thames Valley; offices and warehouses in Liverpool, London and Birmingham; chemical works in Liverpool and banks in Bangor, Caernarvon and Chester, he was able to rule the world market in copper with an 'iron' hand.

Thomas Williams admitted to a House of Commons committee in 1799 that he was worth almost a million pounds, and that half the world's copper industry was in his hands alone. What he didn't tell them was that from 1791 onwards, the control of his empire had been gradually slipping from his grasp, and in a relatively short time his empire dwindled to almost nothing. His health broke and he died in Bath, leaving his grieving widow Catherine, his two sons John and Owen, and three daughters, one of whom was Margaret. He left bequests of £92,000 to each of his daughters (presumably so they could be more attractive to suitors), £20,000 to his younger son, and an estate worth £10,000 a year to his elder son. His body was brought back to Anglesey to be buried at the old Llanidan church but was removed to Llandegfan churchyard in 1832, where his son Owen was buried in the same grave the next day.

Amongst his descendants was the Welsh artist Sir Kyffin Williams, whose last purchase before his death in 2006 was a portrait of Thomas Williams.

One of the greatest disappointments regarding such a man as Thomas Williams is that there is no fitting memorial for him in his home country, and he is now largely forgotten.

Some movers and shakers, like Williams, were local people or those with a local connection, such as Sir Nicholas Bayly (first mentioned in Chapter 3). In 1753, Bayly leased part of the Parys Farm land from Lewis for £25 per annum. Neither realised what lay beneath their feet, and neither bothered much about the boundaries, until the legal argument about their rights to the land. The settling of this dispute by Thomas Williams resulted in both Williams and Bayly making a fortune. Nicholas Bayly died in 1782, eighteen years after his wife Caroline. Both are commemorated by a plaque in Llanedwen Church, Anglesey.

Many of the movers and shakers moved to Amlwch from elsewhere. A few were from the cradle of the Industrial Revolution in the north of England or from the Midlands, and many others from south-west England, where they had gained valuable experience by working in the tin mining industry. Some of those were:

John Dawes, one of Thomas Williams' business partners, the London banker who bought the Plas Newydd share of the Mona Mine.

Captain Charles Dyer (1803–1879), mine manager at Parys Mountain from 14 April 1858 until his death ('Captain' was an honorary title). He was a Devonian by birth but had worked in the Northop Lead Mines in

Flintshire as an engineer before coming to Amlwch to live in Parys Lodge. He had a wide range of interests which included politics, religion (he was treasurer of his local chapel), socialising and science (a member of the Amlwch Scientific Society). Under his management the Parys Mine Company made a profit of £400,000 between 1857 and 1879. After his death the company's profits nosedived and it was forced to close in 1910.

Alexander Fraser (first mentioned in Chapter 3), believed to have been born sometime between 1663 and 1667. He was educated at the King's College, Aberdeen. He had to leave Scotland in a hurry after the suspicious death of a piper in 1692. He eventually arrived in Anglesey in 1761 and worked for Sir Nicholas Bayly, and is credited with the discovery of copper ore on Cerrig y Bleiddiau land.

John Wynne Paynter (1815–1883), brother of William Cox Paynter, owner of the Far Side Shipyard in Amlwch Port. John was born in Maes Llwyn, Amlwch and educated at the Beaumaris Grammar School. The family had hopes that he would qualify as a doctor and work for the 'Welsh Company' on Parys Mountain, but together with Thomas Fanning Evans, John leased the Mona Mine Company for over thirty years from 1866 onwards. He also built Mona Mill, the largest wind-powered flour mill on Anglesey (seven floors, four pairs of grinding stones) in 1816. He was also a chapel elder and leading hymn singer for over fifty years at the local Wesleyan chapel.

Charles Roe (1715–1781), founder of Roe & Co. (Macclesfield Copper Company), was considered one of the great industrialists of his period. He was born in Castleton, Derbyshire, the son of a parish priest, but on being orphaned he moved to Macclesfield. His first successful business venture was in the silk market, from which he moved into copper mining and smelting in 1758. Much of his fortune was invested in Macclesfield in Cheshire, and in the Lake District. He moved to Anglesey in 1763, when he obtained a twenty-one year lease to develop the Mona Mine on Parys Mountain. Although he lost the lease in 1786, Roe & Co. was responsible for much of the development of the Parys Mine Company. Roe & Co. also worked in the Avoca copper mines in Ireland. After Charles's death, his son William took partial control of the company.

Captain Thomas Tiddy, works manager at Parys Mountain, was appointed to the post by James Treweek in 1819, but resigned his post when the miners went on strike in protest against the introduction of a new method of payment. He was never a popular figure on Parys Mountain and once, when in hiding in the Carreg y Doll Engine House, he was very, very scared when the boiler exploded. The miners were in a prayer meeting at the time and Divine Retribution became a popular topic of conversation in Amlwch for weeks following the explosion!

George Trewren (1812–1876), a Cornishman from the parish of St. Blazey, was the mine agent who succeeded Thomas Tiddy in 1860. For a short time he lived at Bodgadfa, Penrhyd, Amlwch. His greatest mistake was in favouring William and George, the Buzza brothers ('Buzza' is an old Cornish name). He was accused of accepting their terms for a bargain after he had rejected a better one from the Welsh workers. A strike meeting was called. Owen Roberts, the strike leader, was dismissed, though later reappointed. Trewren and the Buzza brothers left Parys Mountain.

Only a few, other than Thomas Williams and Sir Nicholas Bayly, could claim to be Amlwch or Anglesey born and bred. This group included men such as:

Thomas Fanning Evans (1841–1891), born at Mona Lodge, Amlwch, who followed in his father's footsteps to work in the mountain. Evans was appointed Government Mine Inspector for north Wales; according to one tale he was offered the post when his interviewer suddenly realised that Fanning Evans knew more about mining than he did. He was well-liked and respected by the workers because, during a very difficult period, he abolished all debts to the company. In 1880 his name was put forward as a parliamentary candidate but due to a clash of interests he withdrew and concentrated on forming the successful Parys Mine Company. In his later years he was appointed Justice of the Peace and High Sheriff for the county of Anglesey. He died while on a visit to Ireland but was brought home to Amlwch to be buried.

John Price (1754–1804), chief mining agent at the Mona Mine, and co-founder of the Amlwch Shipping Company in 1786 with Stephen Roose of the Parys Mine Company.

John Price (1780–1855), as his father and grandfather before him, was chief mining agent at the Mona Mine.

Details of the
Amlwch and the Celebrated Mona and Parys Copper Mines Corrected and enlarged; Printed by Enoch Jones, Wrexham Street, Beaumaris: 1848

MONA MINE AGENTS
Head Agent – JAMES TREWEEK, Esq., who has the general control, and conducts the financial matters of the Mona Mine and Smelting Works.
Pit-Work & Engineering – Captain T. Tiddy.
Surface & Underground Operations – Mr J. H. Treweek.
Ore-dressing and other Departments – Captain Job.
Assay Chemist – Mr W. G. Treweek.
Assistant – Mr Thomas.
Principal Accountant – Mr E. Evans.

PARYS MINE
Head Agent – C. B. Dyer, Esq., who has general control and conducts the financial affairs of this mine.
Surface & Other Departments & Underground Operations – Mr C. E. Dyer.
Assay Chemists – Mr H. Roberts & Mr John Dyer.

SMELTING WORKS
Principal Refiner & Agent – Mr Edward Reese.
Agent for other Departments – Mr William Hughes.
Accountant – Mr John Jones, who is likewise Collector of Harbour Dues.

---

[1] *The Copper King.* J. R. Harris, Landmark Publishing, 2003.

[2] *Ibid.*

[3] *Ibid.*

[4] *Ibid.*

[5] *Copper Mountain, op. cit.*

[6] *Ibid.*

6

A community of workers

In the rough, tough world of mining at Parys Mountain a community of remarkable workers lived and worked together: the 'Copper Ladies'. Many have been forgotten, and their work on the mountain is their only memorial, but others, for different reasons, left a lasting impression.

The Copper Ladies were employed to wield hammers and break down the ore brought to the surface into smaller, more manageable lumps. They would boast that this was not hard work, as they were used to long hours of farm or house work, and spinning wool before starting on their shifts on the mountain. Between sixty and eighty women would work together in a noisy wooden shed. Sitting on three-legged stools, they would face each other, talk and banter, and order about the children who served them with baskets of ore. For their labour, they were paid 10d per 12-hour shift or 6 shillings a week, which was twice what a farm labourer was earning at the time. If lucky, they were also paid a pension of 1/6 a week after their working lives ended.

> Maent oll yn ferched medrus
> A hwylus hefo'u gwaith,
> A'u henwau geir yn barchus
> Gan fwynwyr o bob iaith;
> Hwy weithient oll yn galed
> Am gyflog bychan iawn –
> O'r braidd cant drigain ceiniog
> Am weithio wythnos lawn.[1]

[They are all skilful women
And adept at their work;
The miners of different countries
Speak very highly of them;
They all work hard
For a very small wage –
Earning only five shillings
For a full week's work.]

What drew the public's attention to the Copper Ladies was their mode of dress. Fashion was not important to them; practicality was what counted. They scared little children, with a big, metal studded glove on one hand and a 4-pound hammer in the other. A petticoat of homespun material was worn under a skirt and a leather apron. A yellow scarf kept the dust from their hair and dirt from their ears. The scarf was topped with a black hat. On their feet they usually wore a pair of clogs, made locally in Llannerch-y-medd or Penysarn. These wooden-soled clogs lasted much longer than any other material in the acidic atmosphere of the work shed. By their side was a 'knock stone' on which the lumps of ore were broken.

According to Census Returns for the period of fifty years between 1841 and 1901, Copper Ladies ranged from seventy-three years old (Modlan Jones from Penysarn) to eleven years old (Ellen Hughes of Tŷ Popty, Parc Llandyfrydog).

It would appear that breaking the ore was work for the younger women, though the impression one gets from reading about them was that all Copper Ladies were mature women. The longest-lived Copper Lady was probably Abigail Nearney/Nurney, ninety-five years old at the time of the 1881 Census. She was originally from Ireland but lived in a tied cottage in the Mona Yard on the mountain with her daughter Ann, forty-six years old, and listed as Yard Keeper. Abigail died in 1885 and was buried with her husband in Amlwch Public Cemetery:

> In affectionate Remembrance of JOHN NURNEY,
> Who died February 1st 1875 Aged 78 years.
> ALSO of ABIGAIL NURNEY, his wife, who died
> October 16, 1885, Aged 101.

The various house names make an interesting study: Carreg Cwrnach (*cwrnach*: a metallic/ore-bearing stone), Cerrig y Bleiddia' (*cerrig*: stones; *bleiddiau*: wolves), Dyffryn Coch (*dyffryn*: valley; *coch*: red) describing the colour of the local soil and water in the river flowing from the mountain), Hen Waith (*hen*: old; *gwaith*: work/works – an indicator of past efforts), Llaethdy (*llaethdy*: dairy – indicating an agricultural background), Lletro(e)d (a footprint, or a foot's width), Llyn Coch (*llyn*: lake), Maen Dryw (*maen*: rock; *dryw*: wren), Rhwngc (possibly from '*rhwng*' = between), Tavern Spite (*tavern y spite* = 'spite' from 'hospital', or a place of rest), Tŷ Popty (*tŷ*: house; *popty*: bakery). Many of the above names have survived into the twenty-first century. No mention of a works barracks is made, although some did live on site in Brimstone Yard, Mona Yard and on Parys Mountain.

Though universally known as 'Copper Ladies', only in the 1881 Census were they actually noted by that name. Otherwise their profession is listed as Copper Breaker, Copper Dresser, Copper Ore Picker, Cutting Copper, Picking Copper in the Mine or Working in the Copper Mine.

One of the Copper Ladies, Phoebe Morris, was described as a very respectable old lady, clumsy, fat, heavy, and a bass singer for the Ladies' Choir. Unfortunately her voice was compared to that of a calf, or a man suffering from a bad cold, but as powerful as two men singing together. She could be heard from a distance, making more noise than the circular saw used in the yard. And yet, someone else described her as being very musical, and a skilled poetess.

Beti Jones was another Copper Lady and the area's only midwife. It is said that she kept a teapot on her mantelpiece containing 1300 dried peas – one for every baby that she had delivered.

Of all who deserve a mention in the chronicles of Parys Mountain, Catherine Randall stands out and yet, if one was to ask about her in 2011, few would know of her by her proper name. To the Welsh-speaking community, she was much better known as 'Cadi Rondol'. She was, probably, the best-known of the Copper Ladies.

Cadi was a character in the true meaning of the word. Few details and facts about her have survived, but what little we know is well worth repeating. She was the youngest daughter of John and Jane Randall, a family who had moved to Amlwch to look for work. They lived at Parc Bach, near Glanrafon, Penysarn. Jane was buried on 2 September 1794.

Cadi was born in 1743 and worked on the mountain from 1761 onwards. She paid 2 shillings a week rent for a cottage on the estate of the 2nd Marquess of Anglesey in Dyffryn Coch. To live and survive in Amlwch in the late eighteenth century one had to have a strong character and constitution. Cadi certainly had all the necessary requirements. She made her living as a copper lady and as a prostitute. Her profanities could be heard all over town, and she would use her fists to settle any argument. John Jones (1762–1822), one of the elders of Capel Mawr (*capel*: chapel; *mawr*: big), Amlwch, was bold enough to tell her off for misbehaving and using strong language in public. He was told to mind his own business and was threatened by Cadi's knife!

Cadi 'found religion' when she was forty-five, during a service held at Capel Mwd, Pengraigwen, in about 1788. Such was the strength of her new convictions that it is said that neither Methodism nor Cadi will be forgotten in Anglesey as long as there is someone to tell one story or another. She became a committed member of Lletroed chapel and would walk miles to attend services all over the island. When one of the Amlwch residents reminded her of her colourful past, she admitted her sins but said that she was whiter than white by then, even whiter than Mary Magdalene. Cadi was so excited by one sermon at Llanfwrog Chapel that she jumped up on the seat and danced in ecstasy. Unfortunately, the seat collapsed under her weight!

She left the yard on Parys Mountain and worked as a feather collector, calling at different farms to collect a good supply for stuffing pillows. Many a farm mistress would invite her to sit at the kitchen table to eat with the family. In the house called 'Vitriol', home of a Mr Webster, Cadi refused to sit and eat at the table, saying she preferred to sit at the Lord's Table and partake of his Body and Blood. When asked by Webster if her devout praying had brought any response from the Good Lord, her reply was, 'No, otherwise you would have changed your ways!'

In 1800, aged fifty-seven, she found employment at the house and shop of the Reverend John Elias and his wife in Llanfechell. She was told off by Mr Elias for singing a lullaby to the baby, and it was suggested to her that a hymn would be a much better choice. Her reply was that she would rather not sing to a baby praises that should be due to the Lord – even if the baby was Mr Elias' son! Tradition has it that on another occasion, after attending a chapel service, that she asked Mr Elias, *'Ai am fy meiau i dioddefodd Iesu Mawr?'*

(Was it for my sins that Jesus died on the cross?) This became the first line of John Elias' most famous hymn.

When Cadi lay on her death bed, John Elias, with John Hughes (*Siôn Huws*) from Tŷ'n Caeau (one of the devout men who worked in the mine – he was also known as *Siôn Huws Yr Haleliwia*), visited to help ease her passing. On entering the house, they enquired if she was there by herself. Cadi replied, 'No, not by myself, as He is always here.'

She died aged eighty-five, and was buried on Wednesday 20 February 1828. The funeral costs were paid by Mr Webster, who even offered to pay for a hearse to carry her on the final journey, but his offer was refused as she had so many (religious) brothers from amongst the Methodists to carry her. Unfortunately, no one paid for a gravestone, so her final resting place is unknown.

To list all the men that worked on the mountain would be a very laborious task as over 500 were named in the 1841 Census alone. Many lived in the Tredath area of Amlwch. On looking at such lists, one cannot help but ask if the Frazer family, some of whom lived at Fron Heulog, Rhosybol, others at Twrllachiad, Llanwenllwyfo, and one at Glan Gors, Llaneilian, were related to Alexander Frazer. Were William and Edward Allen of Ponc Taldrwst related to Thomas Allen? Thomas Allen's gravestone tells us that he was 'caught by Death' in the Rhos Manach (*rhos*: heath; '*manach*' = '*mynach*': monk) mine on 2 January 1839 and buried at Llaneilian churchyard.

What became of the Gibbon family, whose name has now disappeared altogether from the Amlwch area? Other uncommon surnames have survived: was Mr Chard originally from Somerset? Farm and house names have also survived, such as Virgin House, Llanwenllwyfo; Cwna (to erect or to build), Llanwenllwyfo; Grogan Goch, Amlwch.

Were there ever wolves in Cerrig Bleiddia? Who was the Ithal that had a barn named after him in Sgubor Ithal?

The most notorious character who worked on Parys Mountain was Thomas Edwards. Edwards was 6 foot 2 inches in height, very strong, and, according to the *Shrewsbury Chronicle* of 18 September 1813, had been known as 'King of the Mountain' at Parys Mountain. He was otherwise known, and is still remembered by some, as *Yr Hwntw Mawr* (the big southerner). *'Hwntw'* is a nickname usually given to south Walians, but in reality Edwards was from Herefordshire. As he had learnt Welsh, his accent may well have sounded different and led to him being mistaken for a southerner. He worked at Parys Mountain for fourteen years. He was well-known in Anglesey, and became so also in Merionethshire, where he committed a horrific murder.

After leaving Amlwch, Edwards worked on the storm-damaged Cob at Porthmadog. There he learnt of the Penrhyn Isaf family and believed them to be wealthy farmers. Mary Jones, from Caergraig, Llanfrothen, was employed as a maid on the farm of Penrhyn Isaf, Minffordd, near Penrhyndeudraeth. The 18-year-old stayed in the kitchen making oatcakes whilst the family were out harvesting the corn on the afternoon of 7 September 1812. Thomas Edwards had gone to Penrhyn Isaf to steal money. He was seen by Mary with his hand in the dresser drawer, and to prevent her testifying against him, he killed her with a pair of sheep shears.

After hiding his booty in a sheepfold, Edwards washed his hands of Mary's blood in the well before returning home to Tancastell. Mary's body was found by her employer's nephew. The authorities were called and a search for the offender was organised. One woman was so frightened to hear there was a murderer at large that she sought overnight shelter at a neighbour's house – that neighbour was Edwards himself! She noticed deep scratches on his face.

Early next morning, Edwards went to retrieve the stolen money, but was seen and chased. He attempted to escape over the River Dwyryd at Abergafran, but was caught. In the mêlée in the river, Mary's uncle was drowned. Edwards was taken to Dolgellau Gaol by six policemen, but on his way he complained that the chains on his wrist were too tight. As soon as they were loosened, he escaped, and for three days hid in the woods in Penrhyndeudraeth. After being re-arrested, he was taken to Dolgellau by horse and cart. The trial was held in Bala, and to make sure that there would be no further mishaps, John Humphreys, the blacksmith, was paid 2s 7d for a pair of handcuffs.

Yr Hwntw Mawr was hanged in Merionethshire on 17 April 1813. Poor Mary was buried in the churchyard of Llanfrothen.

The gravestone of Owen Griffith (1851–99) in Llanwenllwyfo Churchyard divulges very little about his life. He is remembered as a faithful and hardworking deacon of Bozrah Calvinistic Methodist Chapel, Penysarn, but not a word is mentioned about his term of work on Parys Mountain. And yet he was one of the most important characters who ever set foot on the mountain. He started working underground in the mines when only nine years old for a wage of a groat (4d) a day for a 12-hour shift. On making his way to the mine on his first morning at work, he called at his grandmother's house to enquire if she had an old hat that would suit him. She found him a hat so tall that even if he went on his hands and knees it would have knocked on the tunnel ceiling! She suggested that Owen should visit the carpenter, Huw Gruffydd, and ask him to saw a few inches off!

Owen worked underground, and later as a supervisor, manager, secretary and inspector of the Smelting Works in the mine, before resigning to become a merchant, shopkeeper, poet, chapel elder, musician, singer, *codwr canu* (precentor), alderman and author. His literary efforts were restricted to only one volume, but that volume is recognised as a very illuminating history of the Parys Mountain Copper Works.

Rhisiart Lewis was one of many who made sure his son followed him to work on the mountain. His son Lewis William Lewis (1831–1901), the second of six children who were born in one of the houses on Stryd Tai Mwd (*stryd*: street; *tai*: houses; *mwd*: mud), Penysarn, became much better known as Llew Llwyfo.

Llew's schooling was mostly in Sunday School and his text book was *Y Rhodd Mam* (*rhodd*: gift). He started work when he was eight years old and was promoted to the responsible post of ore sampler when he was only eleven. Due to his youth he suffered quite a lot from bullying by much older workmen and he left at fourteen, to be apprenticed a clothier and draper at Bangor and Holyhead. He married a Holyhead girl and moved back to open a shop in Penysarn and Llaneilian in 1852. He also worked as a storeman for Nicholas Treweek in Amlwch Port. He left Anglesey for the USA in 1868 on a singing tour. The poet D. Gwenallt Jones has described him as the most multi-talented man of the nineteenth century. On his return to Wales he drifted from place to place and from job to job. He is remembered as a composer, musician, singer, translator and traveller, and was described on his death certificate as a journalist and vocalist. He suffered from asthma and gangrene, and died at his son's house at 12 Greenfield Street, Millbank, Rhyl, on 23 March 1901. He was buried in Llanbeblig, Caernarvon.

Owain Hughes, Cerrig Man (1896–1985) was one of the last workers at the *pyllau paent* (precipitation pits). His recollections have been included in *Mynydd Parys* by Gwyn Parry & Steve Makin:

When I started work in the mountain
I was 17 years old. I worked on level 45 fathoms
I never could go down further, me that is.
I used to start at 6 and finish at 5,
that was when I started in 1913.

I worked in the water, you know,
scrap iron and that, copper precipitate and paint.
I pumped water into the mountain
I went to the old workings where the water could not reach.
With water in pipes I sprayed the rock
to strengthen the precipitate.

They got ochre from the pools at Pentrefelin, you know,
I remember the paintworks in Amlwch,
I remember it standing, you know, on its feet
a huge chimney on it.

With water I went down the shafts
ropes and footwires down,
one ladder then another,
footwires they called them.
There were 800 men underground,
My dad was an engine driver,
pumped water to relieve the engines
all his life.
I pumped water out all day.
all wet when I had been down the level.

When I was 20, the war,
the First World War.
We were working the garreglas,
blende ore in English.
I was the youngest there, as I know it.

Too many went away to fight,
boys from Llanfechell, Llaneilian.
I was sent to Ypres.

Well, there was nothing important here, you know,
just poor;
poor wages.

---

[1] *Mynydd Parys*. Owen Griffith. Cwmni'r Wasg Genedlaethol Gymreig Caernarfon, 1897.

7

Artists, authors and cartographers

In its heyday, the copper works on Parys Mountain and the harbour at Amlwch Port attracted all sorts of visitors. It was almost magnetic in its appeal, and in those camera-less days some of the artists who made the journey to Anglesey could have replenished their stock of brown ochre powder paint, as it was manufactured on site at the rolling mill in Pentrefelin, situated between the mountain and the town.

The paintings that survive to the present day portray scenes from a period of great changes that would have been unrecorded were it not for the artists' work. They show how the greenness of the mountain was lost to a multi-coloured industrial influence. Many of the artists who painted scenes of Parys Mountain concentrated on the Great Opencast as it was the most striking of sights. Another feature of a number of the paintings is the smoke which was also commented upon by the visiting writers. All the artists mentioned below painted Parys Mountain.

One of the most memorable paintings of that period is John Warwick Smith's 1792 portrayal of the Mona Yard, showing the gloom of the work yard with pastoral Anglesey seen in the distance and the mountains of Snowdonia even further away. He helps the viewer bridge the gap between an industrialised site and the relative peacefulness of the surrounding countryside.

A painting by Warington Wilkinson Smythe, an eminent artist and geologist of his time, shows the mountain as only a geologist could appreciate it. Warington Smythe (1817–1890) worked as an Inspector of Mines. He was a noted author and expert in his field of study as well as a talented artist.

William Daniell (1769–1837) earned a reputation as an artist and engraver. He was born in Kingston-upon-Thames. His father kept The Swan public house in Chertsey. After his father's death in 1779 Daniell went to live with an artist uncle. They travelled to China and India in 1785, where they sold their paintings to fund the journey. They returned to England in 1794. In 1819 William published a volume about their travels. He spent the years between 1814 and 1825 travelling around the British coast with Richard Ayton. He produced more than 300 paintings which filled eight volumes. His most famous work includes scenes of the West Indies Docks in London and a painting depicting the Battle of Trafalgar. His best-known painting of Amlwch Port, painted from the rocks of Trwyn Penwaig (Herring Head) leading down to the sea, shows a small ship entering the harbour with a forest of masts in the near distance and Parys Mountain on the horizon.

Moses Griffith (1769–1809) was one of the few Welsh artists whose works depict scenes of Parys Mountain. He was born in Bryncroes, Gwynedd, and was from a very poor background. His early education was almost non-existent, but his talent with a pencil soon became apparent. At twenty-two years of age he was employed by Thomas Pennant and remained with his patron until his death in 1798. Pennant wrote the literary descriptions of their journeys, whilst Griffith's paintings were used to illustrate the published volumes. Late in his life, Griffith lived in Holyhead and was employed as an engraver by Francis Grose.

William Havell (1782–1857) was the son of a Reading Grammar School art teacher. In 1804 he moved to London to live and his work was exhibited at the Royal Academy. He travelled to the Lake District in 1807, painting on his way, on a year-long journey that also brought him to Wales. He was one of the founders of the Society of Watercolour Artists. He died on 16 December 1857 in London. Havell's paintings of Parys Mountain show workers being lowered down on ropes into the Great Opencast, with those that have reached the bottom so small in size that they convey how great and deep a chasm the Opencast was.

Julius Caesar Ibbetson the Elder was born on 29 December 1759 in Leeds, and named in honour of the Roman emperor (he was a Caesarean baby). He served an apprenticeship as a marine painter in Hull. On moving to London his work was exhibited at the Royal Academy from 1785 onwards. He travelled to China, the Cape of Good Hope, Madeira and Java, but returned to London on the death of his employer and produced many landscapes in oils and watercolour. He travelled through Wales in 1792 with John Warwick Smith and Robert Fulke Greville. Following the journey he published a volume of engravings titled *A Picturesque Guide* (1793). He died on 13 October 1817.

Sir Thomas Lawrence (1769–1830) had a hard life. He was the talented son of a Bristol publican who, in 1779, was declared bankrupt. Thomas became the family provider. The family moved to Bath and Thomas worked as a portrait artist. His portrait of Thomas Williams shows a well-dressed man standing in what might well be a drawing room in his home at Llanidan Hall, with a determined look on his face and the headland of Penmaenmawr in the distance. Lawrence journeyed through Europe in 1818 gaining a reputation as a gifted artist. On his return to London in 1820 he was elected president of the Royal Academy, a post he held until his death in 1830.

Edward Pugh (1761–1813) was born in Ruthin, but spent most of his working life in Chester and London. He specialised in landscapes. His most famous work was *Cambria Depicta*, a record of his journey through north

Wales containing over seventy paintings, including *The Confluence of the Parys and Mona Mines* (1792) and *Parys Mines* (1804). He was working on the volume in his final weeks, completing nine years' work. It was published after his death in 1816, and is considered to be the finest-ever travel journal of north Wales. Another famous work is his portrait of the playwright Thomas Edwards (Twm o'r Nant).

John Warwick Smith (1749–1831) was born in Irthington, Carlisle. His patron was the Earl of Warwick, whose name he adopted. He travelled throughout Italy and Britain and published volumes of engravings such as *Select views in Great Britain* (1812), *Views of the Lakes of Cumberland* (1791–5), *Tour through Wales* (1794), and *A tour to Hafod* (1810). In 1805 he was accepted as member of the Society of Watercolour Artists. During Smith's tour through Wales he saw the castles of Dinefwr, Pembroke, Carreg Cennen and Caernarfon, among others. His paintings show parts of Wales before the Industrial Revolution; Aberystwyth, before the arrival of the railway in the 1860s, is shown by him as a very small, isolated town on Cardigan Bay.

A number of cartographers came to Amlwch to see Parys Mountain and study the landscape, to enable them to draw maps of the area or for estate and land owners. Among them was an unnamed cartographer of the time of Elizabeth I who drew a map showing the site and position of the harbour, the town and the copper works. As each new map appeared the quality of the work improved.

Most of the literary visitors wrote in English. They were usually members of the landed gentry who could afford to travel to Anglesey. Some have even been labelled 'professional travellers' by D. Morgan Rees. They, like other visitors to Amlwch and Parys Mountain, must have stared in wonder at the sights before them.

Arthur Aitkin (1773–1854) was a chemist, miner, traveller and a scientific author who was born in Warrington, Lancashire. He studied chemistry under Joseph Priestly, specialising in practical science. In 1807 he was a founder member of the Geological Society in London and was the society's secretary from 1812 to 1817. He kept detailed records of all his travels, and published *Journal of a Tour through North Wales and Part of Shropshire with Observations in Mineralogy and Other Branches of Natural History* in 1797.

He was much impressed by what he saw of Amlwch Port:

> We were much pleased with seeing the scars of rock between the town and the sea, occupied by numerous groups of men, women and children, all neat and tidy and in their best clothes, it being a Sunday, who were enjoying the mild temperature of a summer evening, redeemed refreshing by the neighbourhood of the sea ... Out of the whole number we did not see one drinking party ... most of the miners are Methodists, and to the prevalence of this religious sect is chiefly to be attributed the good order that is conspicuous.

What he saw and heard on the mountain must have been quite awe-inspiring:

> The substance of the mountain being ore, the work is carried on in a very different manner from the custom of other mines. Here are comparatively few shafts or levels, the greater part being quarried out for as to leave a vast excavation open to the day. There are two of these

quarries or mines which are worked by two different companies. The first goes by the name of Mona Mine and is the sole property of Lord Uxbridge. The other called Parys Mine is shared between the Earl and Mr Hughes.

The view down this steep and extensive hollow is singularly striking. The sides are chiefly of a deep yellow or dusty slate Colour, streaked however, here and there, by fine veins of blue or green, shooting across the cavern, mingles with seams of greyish yellow. The bottom of the pit is no means regular, but exhibits large and deep burrows in various parts, where the richer vein has been followed in preference to the rest. Every corner of this excavation resounds with the noise of pickaxes, hammers: the edges are lined with workmen drawing up the ore from below: and a short intervals is heard, from different quarters the load explosion of the gunpowder by which the rock is blasted, reverberated in pealing echoes from every side.

Richard Ayton (1786–1823), an author, playwright and sailor, was the travelling companion of William Daniell (see above). They produced *A Voyage round Great Britain, undertaken in the Summer of the Year 1813*: Ayton wrote the prose; Daniell was the engraver. Ayton's description of Parys Mountain is considered a classic:

On every part of its surface the hill is as bare as the public road. No kind of vegetation can live in this sulphureous atmosphere; not a weed, not lichen on the rocks has been spared. We were amazingly struck with the first view of the mine, which is truly an astonishing monument of human industry. The mine has been worked like a stone quarry, and an immense crater has been formed nearly a mile in circumference; and in many parts, three hundred feet in depth. As we stood upon the verge of this tremendous chasm, it appeared to us like a mighty work of nature, produced by some great convulsion, but, certainly, suggested to our minds nothing so mean as the pick-axe and the spade. There were but few people at work, and their figures, discovered here and there among the huge rocks, looked merely as flies upon a wall, and one could scarcely imagine that, by these little creatures, each picking its little hole, the mountain had been thus demolished. The sides of the mine are mostly perpendicular, but the bottom is broken and irregular, and penetrated in various parts, by wide and deep hollows, in which veins of peculiar richness have been followed.

The Reverend William Bingley (1774–1823) was born in Doncaster and educated at the local grammar school and St Peter's College, Cambridge. In 1814 he published two volumes of work on his 1798 journeys through north Wales:

Hundreds of men, women and children, appeared busily occupied in the different branches of this vast concern and the bustle of metropolis prevailed amidst the dreary recesses of the Druids.

We were first conducted to some wooden stages erected on the edge of an immense excavation of an oval form about two hundred yards long, half as much in width and eighty in depth which has been hollowed out in course of twenty years. On looking down from hence to the chase beneath, we saw the rock rich with ore of a light gold colour which the miners were busily engaged in boring, blasting, breaking with sledge hammers, wheeling the fragments to appointed places beneath the stages filling the baskets which were hauled up by windlass.

There might be from twelve to fourteen stages erected for this purpose in different parts of the mine. As soon as the commodity is landed it is delivered to a number of women and children to be broken into smaller pieces, the good ore is then separated from that of an inferior sort and carried to the kilns to be baked the sulphur forms in what is called flour brimstone ... collected, melted in large cauldron and formed into round moulds for sale. We understood that the better type of ore was sent to Neath and other places, and the inferior to the smelting houses in Amlwch.

On the death of his father, Matthew Boulton (1728–1809) bought a plot of derelict land in Soho, Staffordshire, on which he built a mint. In 1773 he entered a partnership with James Watt to develop and sell steam engines of Watts' own invention. Most were sold to coal mine owners to raise water from the mines; they were four times as powerful as similar machines invented by Thomas Newcomen, which were mostly used in coal mines where a plentiful supply of coal was easily obtained. In other mines or works, though, it proved to be an expensive engine to run. James Watt improved on Newcomen's design in 1769, so that the engine used less coal. Watt's engine became a bestseller.

Boulton & Watt steam engines became very popular and they were adapted for a number of other uses in factories and coal mines. Boulton used a steam engine in 1786 in the minting of coins for the British and other governments. He also produced 'Druid Head' coins for Thomas Williams and his companies. Boulton was a leading member of the Birmingham Lunar Society; other members were Watt, Erasmus Darwin, Josiah Wedgwood and Joseph Priestley.

Once a month, when the moon was full, the society met to discuss agricultural, industrial and scientific matters. Boulton's visit to Amlwch was in 1787, when he spent three days observing the copper works and was most impressed: 'Anglesey Copper Mine is a tremendous mine for a Cornish miner to behold.'

Michael Faraday (1791–1867), one of the most eminent scientists of his day, was a blacksmith's son from Newington Butts in Surrey. He was apprenticed as a bookbinder and read as much as he could in his spare time. Because of his interest in science, he was employed by Humphrey Davy in 1813. In 1827 he was appointed science teacher to the Royal Society, and was famous for his experiments with electricity. In 1853 he refused to help the government in developing a poisonous gas to use during the Crimean War.

Faraday wrote to his sister describing the sights of Parys Mountain:

We now dressed. I stripped off everything but my stockings and boots and took possession of a miners trousers, shirt and coat all of thick flannel. Then putting on a thick woollen cap, hanging a candle to my breast button and taking another lighted and garnished with clay in my hand I was now ready to descend. Magrath was similarly equipped and we laughed heartily at each other as a sort of prologue to our adventure.

We were again amused with each others appearance which though comical before was now much heightened by the dirt and water of the mine. At the office we found Mr Irewick waiting for us and soap and hot water ready for use. We stripped, washed and dressed and were soon in complete order again.

All the miners work in flannel clothes and from our own feelings we had reason to commend the custom. We did not feel at all incommoded by heat during our stay below though when we came up and began to change we found ourselves in the very highest state of perspiration. The advantage of flannel arises from the little influence moisture has over it and its non-adhesion to the skin even though damp or moist.

Thomas Pennant (1726–1798) is considered one of the literary giants of north Wales. He is best remembered as a travel writer, antiquary and naturalist. He was the squire of the Downing estate, Whitford, Flintshire. Among his published works are *Tours in Wales, Volume 1*, published in 1778, and *Tours in Wales, Volume 2, including A Journey in Snowdonia*, which was published in 1781. Pennant wrote a description of Parys Mountain and its history up to 1781, and described the smoke and fumes that were so poisonous that not a bird would venture onto the waters of the pools near the mountain.

Robert Roberts (1834–1885) – otherwise known as Y Sgolor Mawr (The Great Scholar) by reason of his impressive self-education – was a cleric and scholar. He was born on 12 November 1834 the son of Owen and Mary Roberts, Hafod Bach, Llanddewi, Llangernyw, Denbighshire. His education amounted to two years' formal learning in Bala and a further two years with a tutor on Anglesey, before he was accepted into a training college in Caernarfon. A teaching career followed in Castell Caereinion and Llanllechid (1853), Amlwch and Ruthin (1855). In Amlwch he was shocked by 'a crowd of boys such as I never saw except in a gutter, half of them had no shoes or stockings, most of them had evidently not been washed for some days past, and all were unruly as wild colts'.

David Thomas (1760–1822) was much better known in Wales by his bardic name of *Dafydd Ddu Eryri*. Though he spent a number of years working in Amlwch he was not happy at all to be there. Dafydd was the son of Thomas and Mary Griffiths, Penybont, Waunfawr, Caernarfonshire, and despite having only eight months' formal education from the curate of Llanberis he proved to be an able scholar. He mastered his mother tongue and the twenty-four measures of strict Welsh poetry, and also English, Greek, Hebrew and Latin. He was apprenticed as a weaver but left to open his own school on 14 July 1787 in Llanddeiniolen. He was also a teacher at Pentraeth, Anglesey. He spent his later years living at Fron Olau, Llanrug. On returning from Bangor, one stormy night, he fell off his horse and drowned in Afon Cegin. He was buried in Llanrug. Many epitaphs were written about him but none mentioned his four miserable years in Amlwch. During his time in Amlwch he worked as a coal measurer but left with many unhappy memories.

> *Nid oes im' einioes ym Mona, – Ow! Myglyd*
> *Yw fy maglog drigfa;*
> *Gwell i Ddafydd bob dydd da,*
> *Lwyddfawr awel y Wyddfa.*

> [There is no life for me in Mona –
> My ragged home is smoke-filled;
> It would be better for Dafydd to spend his days
> Breathing Snowdon's fresh air.]

He composed a further five englynion full of complaints about his life. He felt could not compose poetry while in Amlwch. He did not intend to stay there a minute longer than he had to!

> *Y mynydd, ni ddymunwn – i'w oror*
> *Aros braidd un dwthwn.*

[On this mountainside
I do not wish to spend another day.]

Charles Blacker Vignoles (1793–1875) was an Irish railway engineer who stayed with James Treweek at Mona Lodge, Amlwch for ten days in 1828. The purpose of his visit to was to inspect the works on the mountain. His report concluded that a railway should be built to connect Amlwch Port and the mountain. He estimated the cost at £6,350 per annum and a further yearly £1,000 in maintenance. It proved too high a price for Treweek to consider.

William Withering (1741–1799) the geologist, discovered lead sulphur on Parys Mountain in 1783. This new mineral species, described as 'plumbom (lead) mineralised by vityriolic acid and iron' and later named 'Anglesite' by Beudant in 1832. Withering was born in Wellington, Salop, the son of a surgeon and followed his father into that profession. It was Withering who, in 1792, discovered that 'fairy rings' of mushrooms are caused by the underground *mycelium*.

Morris Williams (1809–1874) was another poet much better known in Wales by his bardic name of *Nicander*. His parents lived at Coed Cae Bach, Llangybi, and he was educated at Llanystumdwy School, but due to the generosity of local bardic sponsors he went to the King's School, Chester and graduated from Jesus College, Oxford. In 1834 he was ordained priest and served as curate of the parish of Holywell, Flintshire. While there he adapted the Book of Common Prayer into Welsh. He also served in Bangor, Pentir and Llanllechid, Amlwch and Llanwenllwyfo (1846–1860) before being appointed rector of Llanrhuddlad, Llanfflewin and Llanrhwydrus, Anglesey. His time in Amlwch was as miserable as *Dafydd Ddu Eryri*'s time in the town. He did not make many friends. He was quite insulting in his comments about his parishioners: `You may have heard the nickname 'Anglesey Pigs'. It is not a nickname at all! Adam himself could not have named them better!'

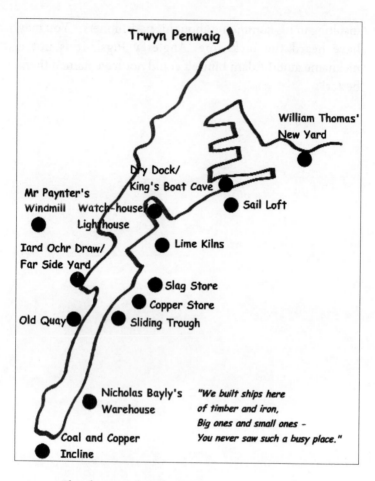

*Sketch map of Amlwch Port in its present form
with some features from its past*

8

Ships and shipbuilding in Amlwch Port

When one facet of industry becomes successful other smaller ones usually benefit. This is exactly what happened in Amlwch when the copper industry blossomed and the shipping industry grew in its wake – quite remarkable considering the state of the harbour. We have read Lewis Morris' comments from 1748; to Thomas Pennant's eye in 1750, it seemed to be a place covered by gorse bushes and grass right down to the shoreline, with goats and sheep grazing on the slopes. Thomas Pritchard described Amlwch Port in 1765 as a small haven for fishing boats to shelter in during a storm.

By 1782 a small pier had been built for the benefit of the Parys Mine Company but the ever-increasing demands on the port and its facilities showed that much more work needed to be done. A 1793 Act of Parliament permitted 'enlarging, deepening, cleansing, improving, and regulating the harbour at Amlwch.'[1] Previously ships had to wait outside the harbour for a berth for hours, sometimes days, so sailing times passed by, tides were missed and financial losses were suffered. The improvements meant that thirty ships of up to 100 tons could be accommodated simultaneously.

A further pier was built in 1816; a small lighthouse in 1817. On the eastern side of the harbour warehouses, coal, metal and ore storage facilities were constructed. Twenty thousand tons of rocks were removed; some were used to build the new pier and to face the dock wall. The rocks were laid in a fashion alien to Anglesey stone workers: that is, they were laid in the Cornish way, with the long side of every stone vertical. A road was built 35 feet above the quay so carters could deliver and off-load ore down wooden chutes into the six large storage bins on the quayside.

Harbour trustees were appointed. They included Thomas Williams, Edward Hughes, Sir John Thomas Stanley, Jonathan Roose and Lord Uxbridge, and other persons who lived within five miles of Amlwch Port and had real estate to the value of £20 or personal property to the value of £300. Their many duties included appointing a clerk, a rates and duties collector, a surveyor and a treasurer, but their most important appointee was the Harbourmaster, who was responsible for directing ships to their allotted mooring berths.

Travellers such as Aitkin, Beer and Bingley were not overly impressed with the improvements, as many ships would lie on their bottoms at low water. This meant that others could not offload or come and go as they pleased. Also, despite all the work done Amlwch Port harbour was still at risk from northerly gales. In 1827 thirteen baulks of timber were used to form a barrier to protect the harbour and vessels from the north wind. The timbers were slotted into grooves between two short piers and acted as a breakwater against waves whipped up by the north and north-east winds.

Other dangers were ever-present. The harbour lighthouse and the one on nearby Point Lynas proved to be ineffective during southerly winds, as smoke from the smelting works obscured both lights, making it very difficult for any vessel to make her way into the port.

The two main factors which benefited the development of the Amlwch copper industry were the demand from the British and other navies for copper sheathing for their ships, and the expanding trans-Atlantic slave trade.

Copper-bottomed ships were easier to steer, faster,

lighter and more manoeuvrable. They also spent less time in dockyards for repairs, as the copper prevented attack by shipworm on the ship's timbers and also prevented fouling by barnacles and weeds. Thomas Williams' companies supplied the copper sheaths and copper bolts that he and two unnamed Birmingham men had helped develop in 1783.

Despite being known as *Twm Chwarae Teg* – Twm Fair Play – Thomas Williams had another side to his character. He was involved in the trans-Atlantic slave trade, and invested considerable sums of money in that industry by building brass and copper works in Holywell, Flintshire, to produce items with which to barter for slaves. He presented a petition against abolition to Parliament in July 1788 demonstrating how much capital he had laid out to get established in the trade (£70,000), and predicting his probable ruin should the slave market be abolished.

The need for copper and ships in Amlwch was increasing almost daily. Sir Nicholas Bayly was already part-owner of the sloop *Sampson* in March 1773, but he needed much more than one small ship for his enterprises. The Parys Mine Company had acquired a few ships by 1782, but not nearly enough to carry sufficient ore to Stanley Works, St Helens and Ravenhead, both managed by Michael, brother of the Reverend Edward Hughes of Llys Dulas. Longer voyages had to be made to the Upper and Middle Bank Works at Swansea and to Penclawdd, as well as sending ore to Birmingham warehouses, Temple Mills in Buckinghamshire, Liverpool, London, chemical works at Garston and to Holywell and Greenfield, Flintshire. Between 1769 and 1717 thirty-five ships and between 1786 and 1789 seventy-one were hired to carry ore from Amlwch. By the late 1780s, Thomas Williams had a personal interest in two Liverpool ships: *Green Linnet*, a seventy-six ton sloop co-owned by himself, John Davies (a London banker) and Michael Hughes; and *Raven*, a seventy-three ton galliot, built at St Helens and owned by himself, John Davies and the Reverend Edward Hughes.

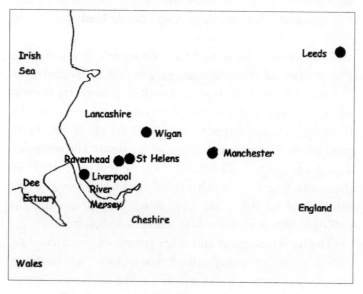

*Sketch map of some important industrial sites
in north-west England*

In 1788 the Amlwch Shipping Company was formed and its members, who included John Price, Mona Mine agent, and Stephen Roose, Parys Mine agent, were managers of the company. They, their company and their ships served the port well – but for only a short period. Other private ventures were founded, with some still-familiar names setting up in the shipping business, such as Roose, Price, Hughes and Howson of Amlwch; Jackson and Percival from Liverpool; David Jones, a Liverpool merchant; Samuel Williams and the Greenfield group; Michael Hughes of St. Helens and David Richards of Swansea – all owners of, or shareholders in, ships regularly seen in Amlwch Port. Some of these ships had homely-sounding names as well: *Maria, Sally* and *Jane*. The *Uxbridge*, a Beaumaris-built, 124-ton brigantine, was probably named in deference to the Plas Newydd family, who had used Uxbridge as their family name since 1714, when Henry Paget was created 1st Earl of Uxbridge. Her master was Robert Roberts, who was in charge for four voyages, carrying one load of 60 tons of ore and three of 100 tons for the Parys Mine Company to Liverpool. On the return voyage, the *Uxbridge* also carried three cargoes of coal, one from Swansea and two from Liverpool to Amlwch.

In 1792 Beaumaris and Amlwch received 327 ships with cargoes totalling 13,287 tons. The figures for the same year in Swansea show that only ninety-six ships used the port facilities there, with cargoes totalling only 5,521 tons. Therefore the harbour in Amlwch dealt with three times as many ships as Swansea.

When James Treweek moved to Amlwch in 1811 he formed a serious connection between the shipping industry and the copper mines. His son Nicholas was set up in business as a coal shipper and gradually became a leading light of the ship-building community in Amlwch. Both he and his brother Francis were commissioned by their father in 1825 to build a sixty-eight ton sloop called *Unity* in the western shipyard or *Iard Ochr Draw* (Far Side Yard), where thirty-two men worked. Another sloop, the sixty-five ton *Marquis of Anglesea*, was built in 1826.

Francis Treweek died in 1832 and his son Nicholas left Amlwch for Liverpool, where he became involved with almost fifty different ships. It was said locally that this was quite an achievement for a man who had started out as a coal merchant! In Liverpool Nicholas was employed as a copper merchant in control of shipments of ore from Amlwch. He

returned to his home town in 1854 after retiring due to ill
health, but was well enough to follow his interest in ship-
building, which had flourished in his absence. He also had
an interest in Canadian-built ships, which he hoped would
compete on the north Atlantic run carrying emigrants on
the way out and timber imports on the return voyages. A
new yard was created for building and repairing ships on the
eastern side of the port, outside the harbour entrance. This
New Yard (*Iard Newydd*) had a dry dock and slipway
facilities. One of the first ships built at the New Yard, and the
first iron-built ship in north Wales, was the 160-ton *Mary
Catherine* launched in 1859.

Treweek's old yard on the Far Side was bought by
William Cox Paynter, who came to prominence as a ship
builder and repairer. The first ship he built on the Far Side
was the *Charles Edwin* for Captain Dyer, a Mona Mine
Company agent at Parys Mountain. Paynter had a sawmill
powered by water from the Red River, which also turned
other machinery at the yard. The river also provided water
to soak ships' timbers so as to prolong their life.

The New Yard, described as an 'Extensive and
Commodious SHIP BUILDING YARD and DRY DOCK',[2]
was bought by William Thomas in May 1872. Due to his
own and his two sons' efforts, over forty ships were built at
Amlwch Port, and were considered by experts such as Basil
Greenhill (Director of the National Maritime Museum at
Greenwich between 1967 and 1983) to be among the best
ever built. William Thomas became one of the leaders of the
ship-building industry not only in Anglesey but far beyond.
But just as the days of the copper mine were numbered, so
were the days of sailing ships. Amlwch Port and its
shipbuilders did not make a successful transition to
steamships. The copper and ship-building industries died a
natural death. Only in the late twentieth century, for a few

short years, was any sort of revival seen in the days of the Anglesey Marine Terminal.

Ships involved in the copper industry or built in Amlwch have been most ably dealt with by authors such as Aled Eames, Bryan Hope and John Rowlands, but a simple list of their names makes very interesting reading. Some of the Amlwch Shipping Company's ships, such as *Eleanor, Mary* and *Kitty*, may well have been named after wives, daughters or girlfriends. Others were a reminder of home, like *Mona* (named after the Mona Mine Company and yard on Parys Mountain) and the *Amlwch*. All were relatively small – averaging 80 tons – with not one being more than 60 feet long.

Almost 120 ships were used to ship copper ore, which was a considerable number for such a small place. Those good times soon faded with the coming of the railway to Amlwch. In 1865, copper ore from Amlwch was moved by rail for the first time. This proved cheaper than using ships, and was another nail in the coffin of the copper and shipping industries. In five years, income from harbour dues fell to 30 per cent of the income in 1860, and the railway became far more important than ships in moving the ore.

---

[1] *Copper Mountain*. John Rowlands, Anglesey Antiquarian Society, 1981.
[2] *A Curious Place: the Industrial History of Amlwch (1550–1950)*. Bryan Hope. Bridge Books, 1994.

Swansea

9

Early days at Neath

Swansea popularly bears the crown as the 'Cradle of Copper Smelting in South Wales from the Time of Queen Elizabeth',[1] but the actual laurels should be firmly placed at Neath.

In a letter dated 22 September 1868 to the *Cambrian* newspaper Grant Francis states that the 'commencement of this important manufacture in our District'[2] was began by The Mines Royal Society at Neath in July 1584. The letter also states that the first copper smelter 'erected upon the river of Swansea'[3] was built by Dr Lane and Mr Pollard in 1717, thus giving Neath a 133-year advantage over Swansea. Other early smelting sites were identified by him as Taibach (built by Newton and Cartwright in the year 1727; the English Copper Company set up a works in 1770, and copper remained an important industry here until Vivian's Copper Mill closed in 1953; the site is now occupied by the town's fire station); Penclawdd (built by John Vivian in the year 1800); Lanelly (built by Daniel, Nevill and others in the year 1805); Loughor (built by Morris and Rees in the year 1809); Cwmavan (built by Vigors & Son in the year 1837); and Pembrey (built by Mason and Elkington in the year 1846).

To chronicle such important events in so little detail is a grave injustice, and a much more detailed picture needs to be painted if we are to understand how one area became a world leader and was honoured with the title of 'Copperopolis'.

According to Henry Hussey Vivian, the story begins with a patent granted by Queen Elizabeth, in 1564, to Thomas

Thurland Jnr, of the Savoy, and Daniel Hogstetter, a German, giving them:

> power to search, dig, try, rost, and melt all manner of mines and ores of gold, silver, copper, and quicksilver in York, Lancaster, Cumberland, Westmoreland, Cornwall, Devon, Gloucester, and Worcester, and the Principalities of Wales, as well within her Majesty's own grounds as other, on payment of a royalty.[4]

Vivian gives credit to Jochim Gans for having devised the most important manner of copper smelting at Keswick in Cumberland in 1581–83. A little earlier, on 21 July 1581, another German-born entrepreneur, Ulricke Frosse, had been sent a letter by Thomas Smith to say that a Mr Westort was going to Cornwall through Wales, and that he would 'take measures for transporting the copper ores to the new melting-house at Neath, in Wales',[5] which he understood to be ready for work. So the exact date of smelting in the area can be set as far back as autumn 1584. Ulricke Frosse was based at Neath by Michaelmas (29 September) of that year. The Mines Royal Society owned the works in Aberdulais, with Ulricke Frosse as manager. The site chosen was close to a waterfall on the Dulais where it joins the Nedd. The falls were chosen to provide water power. The works was situated on land belonging to the Earl of Pembroke, who was also a governor of the Mines Royal Society. Copper ore from St. Ives, Cornwall, was carried across the Bristol Channel. By July 1585 Frosse was smelting 14 hundredweight of ore every day with only one furnace. Work continued until 1598, when the company relocated and moved to Neath Abbey. This site was nearer the sea and ships could be unloaded much closer to the works. Grant Francis, in 1867, placed this site as:

being east and near Neath Abbey Railway Station then occupied by the Mines Royal Works, are on the identical spot where those works were first started ... to which Ulricke Frosse wended his way in the autumn of the year 1584.[6]

During the seventeenth century, coal production in the Neath area was the responsibility of one family in particular: the Evans family. When Herbert Evans died in 1686, Sir Robert Mackworth, a relative through marriage, and the Mine Adventurers of England, took over. They built copper smelters at Melincryddan in 1695 and by 1708 had twenty-two furnaces using the Evans' coal on site. They were known as The Mineral Manufacturers of Neath by 1713. The works was situated on the north bank of the Cryddan River, a much smaller river than the Clydach or the Nedd. Due to its size, a dam was built to feed a leat with water to turn water wheels to work the bellows, grindstones and hammers. The business started off with eight furnaces in 1695 and a Smelting House, which measured 97 feet x 23 feet; a Copper House measuring 36 feet x 22 feet, which had two large copper refining furnaces; and a Stamper Room measuring 24 feet x 7 feet, which housed a 26 feet diameter wheel to drive the stamps to grind the ore and a pair of bellows for smelting.

By 1700 the Smelting House had been extended by 38 feet and a new Refining House, measuring 60 feet x 28 feet containing six refining furnaces, was built. Henry Mackworth had re-formed the Company of Mine Adventurers and in 1702 leased the smelting works to the Company. He was a man of ideas; he used coal from his own mine and built a railway with wooden rails to transport the coal down the hillside; he even experimented with sail power to help the horses move the 18 hundredweight loads.

By 1720 the company was busy using copper and zinc ores to make brass (brass = copper + zinc). Copper and lead ore from Cardiganshire mines were also smelted, as were silver and litharge or lead oxide to be used by glassmakers, potters and apothecaries.

The Melincryddan works was taken over by John Coster in 1731 but he remained there for only eight years before moving to Tai Bach, where a new smelter was built for his use. After Coster's move away, the Melincryddan works was taken over by the English Copper Company who stayed there until 1763. Further expansion had been made by 1766 and the works had doubled in size. By 1779 it was taken over by the Gnoll Copper Company until 1796. Further progress was thwarted, however, when an application for a new lease on the site was refused by Lady Molly Mackworth on the grounds that the works produced far too much smoke, which caused damage to her property. The works was finally closed in 1804, and when an Ordnance Survey map was produced in 1877 it noted only the presence of slag heaps on the site. All other signs of the works had disappeared.

Another company sited at Neath Abbey on the Clydach riverbank was Roe & Co. The company moved to south Wales from Liverpool and Macclesfield in about 1790 and took full advantage of lower labour costs and cheap local coal. They, in turn, were followed by the Cheadle Copper Company until 1821 and the Neath Abbey Iron Company in 1824, which concentrated on ship-building and engineering rather than smelting.

Close to the Mines Royal Works was the Crown Copper Works. Situated on the banks of the Neath, it had been there long enough to be included on a 1797 map and marked as the Red Works. The Rose Copper Company of Birmingham initiated a take-over in 1804. Sometime after 1847 they were taken over by Williams, Foster & Co under a lease from

Lord Dynevor, but by 1866 it was in the hands of Moore & Thomas. During the first few weeks they smelted about 20 tons of ore, but for some reason abandoned the site without warning. The site was then taken over by the Laxey Neath Company, who turned it into a zinc works, but by 1881 activity had ceased.

Production of copper by The Mines Royal Society at Neath Abbey was stopped in 1862 and the works later leased to Williams, Foster & Co., who closed the site down completely in 1881.

Another name for the Clydach Valley at Neath Abbey was Cwmfelin, the site of an old corn mill. There have also been ironworks in the valley, and in 1694 land which housed a furnace to melt iron ore was leased to Thomas Scawen, Esq., of London; Thomas Leeke of Chelsea, Gent.; Thomas Neale, Esq., of London and Benjamin Gyles, mercer (cotton, linen, silk and wool merchant) of London to build a copper battery mill using pig copper from the Mines Royal Society. The battery mill continued in business until 1780 when it converted back to being an iron works.

John Lane, a Bristol chemist, set up a copper smelter in Cwmfelin, north of Tŷ Llwyd. It was not his most successful venture and he moved away to Landore. There, he set up Swansea's first copper works.

---

[1] *The Smelting of Copper in the Swansea District of South Wales from the Time of Queen Elizabeth to the Present Day.* Grant Francis. (Henry Sotheran & Co, 1881).
[2] *Ibid.*
[3] *Ibid.*
[4] *Ibid.*
[5] *Copper Smelting: its History and Processes.* Henry Hussey Vivian. (General Books, 2000).
[6] Grant Francis, *op. cit.,* 1881.

10

Down to the sea: how Swansea became Copperopolis

Swansea has always been a bustling, busy place. It was used as a base for raiding parties by the Norsemen, possibly by the man who gave the town its name: Swein. After the Norman Conquest, a wooden castle was built and a town soon grew. A market was held inside the castle walls. The wooden castle was replaced by one of stone in the thirteenth century, but the town suffered numerous attacks and was set on fire – the last time was in 1402, during the rebellion of Owain Glyn Dŵr. Leather and wool were the main industries of the medieval period. An industry grew to build and maintain the ships needed for the export of the leather and wool, butter, cheese and grain.

Swansea gradually grew into a town with a population of about 2,000 by the 1650s. Coal mining and coal exporting came to prominence. Iron ore was also exported from the port. Three annual fairs were held and the Swansea of 1655 was described by Cromwell as 'a convenient harbour for shipping and resisting any foreign invasions'.

Some had hopes that Swansea could become a seaside resort, a place visited by many. Indeed, many came, including Nelson and Lady Hamilton in August 1802, but even they could not generate enough interest in the town for it to become a holiday resort like those others on the 'English Riviera'. Seventeen years later, visitors wrote:

> Many people resort here in the season for the benefit of sea bathing in consequence of which it has all the concomitants of such places, as Theatre, Library, and Public rooms. We had heard so much of the beauty of the

Town that we were disappointed, it consists principally of a straggling unequal street upwards of a mile in length. The castle, which is used as a jail, is of an ugly colour, but the open and arched parapet arrests the attention. We were recommended by the Gentleman we have before mentioned to the Mackworth Arms Inn as the best in the place and expected therefore some style as well as comfort but were much deceived the house was dirty and gloomy and the people barely civil however they proved their claim to distinction as the great Inn by the extent of their charges.[1]

Swansea missed the boat, as it were, and its fate was to become a copper town.

Swansea was then surrounded by agricultural land and was described in 1795 as being 'ideally situated near the centre of a beautiful bay and on an angle between two hills', but there were other factors which made Swansea ripe for development: it was situated very near to the south Wales coalfield and also on the banks of the Tawe, which was navigable as far as three miles upstream for small sea-going vessels. It was also within easy sailing distance, across the Bristol Channel, of Cornwall and Devon and their copper mines.

Crews of ships sailing to and from south Wales knew well the problems of navigating the estuaries of the Loughor, Tawe, Nedd and Afan rivers. They were shallow and tidal and had no real facilities. The Old Bar at Taibach served the Afan and Ffrwdwyllt rivers. Penclawdd harbour was described as 'difficult', whilst Burry was described as 'treacherous'. Swansea seamen knew very well the advantages of their home port over any other on the south Wales coast. Ships going to Swansea were able to enter the

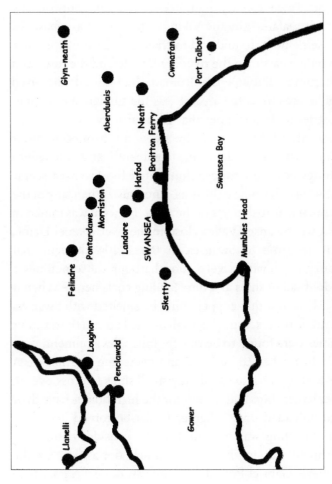

Sketch map showing some important sites in Copperopolis (Swansea)

harbour on the tide earlier than they could enter into Cardiff, and they could leave up to seven hours sooner. The range of the tide at Swansea is not as great as it is in Cardiff or Newport.

The Tawe estuary had been used for centuries by different seafarers: by the Vikings who used it as a base for their settlement, to raid and to trade, and by the Normans, who built a castle on the river bank to defend the town and its harbour. Though the Romans had found and used metallic ores from the area, it was the tinplate and copper industries in Tudor times that gave birth to Swansea as an industrialised town, and the need for proper harbour facilities was realised. In the eighteenth and nineteenth centuries coal and copper dominated the Swansea scene, and Swansea became as busy as, if not busier than, any of the other major British ports of the time. The coal was mined in the Lower Swansea Valley close to the river. Daniel Defoe, when he came to Swansea in the 1720s, thought that 'Swanzy is ... with a very good harbour ... sometimes a hundred sail of ships at a time loading coals here.'[2] When it was discovered that copper could be smelted with Swansea coal, trade routes from Cornwall opened up and the harbour facilities were found to be ripe for much development.

Problems had to be faced and overcome at Swansea. A nine-foot-high bar allowed only small ships to cross over it. Other larger ships had to wait for the high tide or have their cargo unloaded onto a lighter (a flat-bottomed barge). A public meeting was held in 1768 to consider petitioning Parliament but in the face of much opposition by the portreeve, Gabriel Powell, nothing was done. (A portreeve was the chief magistrate of a port or maritime town.) Problems increased when many ships offloaded their ballast as they entered the harbour; sand and mud were continually deposited by the river at its mouth, and when ships lay at anchor waiting their turn to cross the bar, silt built up around them. Dredging had little effect.

In 1787 another attempt to petition Parliament was defeated by Gabriel Powell's opposition, but after his death in 1789 a petition to Parliament to improve the harbour was presented and the Swansea Harbour Act of 1791 passed. One of the most important results of the act was the setting up of a Board of Trustees.

The Harbour Trustees paid Captain Joseph Huddart fifty guineas on top of his expenses to survey the water's edge and suggest improvements, but they chose to ignore most of his suggestions. To their credit they accepted their responsibility for repairing, enlarging and preserving of the harbour. They instigated the deepening of the channels and built piers to prevent silting, on the western bank in 1795 and on the eastern bank in 1809. Another step taken was to erect a double beacon on Mumbles Head in 1791, to show the way into Swansea harbour.

In 1804 Charles and Richard Jamion Nevill had the Burry estuary surveyed again by Captain Huddart. Despite early local opposition they arranged for marker buoys to be placed in the main channels into Llanelli and Penclawdd and for a pilot boat to be on call twenty-four hours a day to guide ships safely ashore. To protect the ships from heavy seas whilst they were in harbour, an extended breakwater was built, and by 1825 the Copperhouse Dock had been completed. Sluice gates had been built to keep water in so that the rise and fall of the tide did not disrupt any loading or unloading. Despite all their efforts, the problem of continuous silting was one they could not defeat.

In 1834 representatives of the English Copper Company and C. R. M. Talbot asked Parliament for an Act to allow the deepening and improving of the Taibach harbour by re-opening an ancient channel to re-direct the Afan and

Ffrwdwyllt rivers. Before 1837 the Afan flowed through the Aberavon Old Bar to enter the sea at a point roughly level with the Somerset Inn at Taibach. In 1824 Mr John Vigurs had opened a horse-drawn tram-road, which ran from his works at Cwmafan along the main highway to Aberavon, and then through Water Street and Ysguthan Road, and then to the Wharf that he had built on the west bank of the Afan. The intention was to use the 'old' channel as a floating dock. This was when the Aberafan Harbour Company was formed. The new docking facilities were opened in 1837 and named Port Talbot.

After Huddart's report in 1804 they again chose to reject his suggestions. With the help of Thomas Telford, John Henry Vivian prepared plans for improving the harbour in 1826–27. These included plans for a floating dock, two basins and a toll bridge over the Tawe. These were refused, but another set of plans was accepted by a new Board of Trustees in 1832. In 1835 permission from Parliament was sought so the work could begin. Five years later, the work started with the opening of a new channel for the river – the New Cut. By 1849 a new floating dock, The Town Float, was ready in the Old Channel. The work was completed by 1851 and the North Dock officially opened on New Year's Day 1852. The dock was closed in 1930 when new facilities were built on the east side of the river, and has since been filled in to accommodate a retail park.

In 1852, the Swansea Dock Company began a private venture, excavating for the South Dock. It was built on the west side of the river, just south of the North Dock. After the Swansea Harbour Trust bought the Swansea Dock Company the work was completed, and on 23 September 1859 the new South Dock was opened. This, according to the *Cambrian* newspaper's correspondent, was 'an event more important than any other in the history of Swansea',[3] but its importance waned and it was closed in 1971 to be redeveloped as a marina, with the surrounding land becoming designated the 'Maritime Quarter' of Swansea.

Three main wharves were established for the copper trade, all situated in the North Dock and managed by Henry Bath & Sons. They were known as Bath's Yard, or Trelandŵr Wharves, Richardson & Co.'s Cobre Yard, and Thomas Elford (later Jose Ford & Co. and eventually Vivians'), known as North Dock Wharf.

The Trustees had the foresight to keep their rates constant at sixpence per ton for a period of twenty-five years from 1855 to 1880, compared with the eleven pence per ton that was being charged at Liverpool. No wonder, then, that the trade involved rose from a quarter of a million tons in 1850 to a million tons in 1876, and that it became one of the world's leading harbours for copper and coal.

In 1879 construction of another new dock, the Prince of Wales Dock, began to the east of the river. It was opened on 18 October 1881 by the future Edward VII, who was Prince of Wales at the time. These facilities were extended in 1898 to twenty-seven acres but its importance did not last; it is now another marina for 500 boats. The King's Dock was opened in 1909 and the Queen's Dock opened by Queen Mary in 1920.

The tasks of moving coal and copper ore products to and from the riverside were major factors in the growth of Swansea as a port. The building of the Swansea Canal was one of the most important steps of all. William Padley surveyed the Tawe valley for a possible canal route. In 1791 an Act of Parliament was passed to authorise the building of the Neath Canal, and as a result a public meeting was held on 5 April 1793 to discuss the possibility of a Swansea canal. Thomas Sheasby was asked to make a survey, but his plans were opposed by the Duke of Beaufort and others who preferred the canal to terminate further up the river at Llandore and Morriston. Swansea Corporation was more in favour of a terminal at Swansea itself, and when they offered to contribute towards the cost, the duke's objections were forgotten and over £50,000 was raised almost immediately.

The duke was allowed to build his own spur (the Trewyddfa Canal) of a mile and a half in length on the canal from Nant Rhydyfiliast to Nant Felin, and charge no more than the company in tolls. Another Act of Parliament permitted the Swansea Canal Navigation Company to raise £60,000 by selling shares, plus another £30,000 should they need it. Permission to build tramways to any place within eight miles of the canal was also granted. All shareholders with five or more shares were on the steering committee. Charles Roberts was in charge of the building of the canal with Thomas Sheasby as his assistant.

In 1798 the Swansea Canal Navigation Company spent almost £60,000 to build the sixteen-mile canal linking the river Tawe and its harbour facilities with the coal mining and metal manufacturing areas of the Swansea Valley. It had thirty-six locks, which raised the waterway by 373 feet. To cross the river at Clydach, Pontardawe, Ynysmeudwy, Ystalafera and Ystradgynlais, aqueducts 65 feet long by 7 feet 6 inches wide were built, to carry loads of up to 22 tons. These fitted well enough into the locks on the main canal, but the Duke of Beaufort had insisted that the locks on the Trewyddfa Section should be only 65 feet long so the boats were an exact fit. The last boat to be built for use on the canal was *Grace Darling*, built in 1918 at Godre'r Graig boatyard.

By the end of the eighteenth century 250 tons of coal per day, as well as other by-products of the copper industry, had to be transported down the valley to the port. Imported ore had to be carried up the valley, so when the sixteen-mile long canal from Swansea to Abercrave was opened it proved of real benefit to everyone. In its heyday, towns such as Abercraf, Clydach, Penwyllt, Pontardawe, Ynysmeudwy, Ystalafera and Ystradgynlais developed and grew by building on the canal's success.

In 1804, 54,235 tons of coal were carried on the canal; in 1816 this had increased to 159,633 tons. In 1825 it was up to 208,433 tons, and by 1839, 386,058 tons.

Competition from the railways was responsible for much of the canal's subsequent decline in fortune. The first suggestion of a railway in the Tawe valley was made in 1830. The Canal Company, desperate to co-operate with the railways in order to maintain some sort of control, agreed to lease the canal to the Welsh Midland Railway for £4,264 a year, but nothing came of the plans. They agreed to lease the canal to the Neath and Brecon Railway for £9,000 a year in 1864, but again the plan foundered.

When the North Dock was completed in 1852 a lock was built to provide a link between the canal and the basin of the new dock. In 1872 the Great Western Railway Company paid £107,666 to the Swansea Canal Navigation Company for the canal and a further £40,000 to the Duke of Beaufort for the Trewyddfa section of the canal near Morriston. A profit was made annually until 1895, but a period of decline followed as the Swansea Vale railway and the Great Western railway took a huge slice of the canal's trade. It made its first loss in 1895; its final profit-making year was 1902. By 1921 the cargo it carried had dwindled to only 10,600 tons. The lower section of the canal was closed and filled in after the First World War, and it was completely closed in 1931 after the last load of coal was carried from Hill's Colliery, Clydach. The canal was nationalised in 1947 and is now in the control of the Canal and River Trust (formerly British Waterways), which has only five of the original sixteen miles of canal to look after.

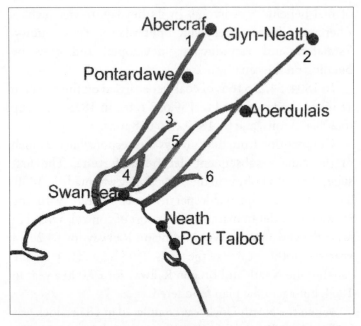

Sketch map showing some of the Swansea and Neath canals
1. Swansea Canal
2. Neath Canal
3. Llansamlet Canal
4. Glan y Wern Canal
5. Tennant Canal
6. Cwrt Sach Canal Branch

The Neath Canal, which stretches for thirteen and a half miles from Glynneath to Melincryddan, Neath, was built in 1795 and extended to Giants Grave in 1799. Other small extensions took it as far as Briton Ferry.

A meeting was held at the Ship & Castle in Neath on 12 July 1790 at which it was agreed to build a canal from Pontneddfechan to Neath, and another from Neath to Giant's Grave. Thomas Dadford was asked to survey a course, assisted by his father and brother. He proposed a route which required twenty-two locks, part of which was a conventional canal, while other parts used the Neath. Dadford estimated the cost at £25,716, but in early 1791 Lord Vernon's agent, Lewis Thomas, suggested alterations to the original plans and the idea of using the river was dropped.

An Act of Parliament passed on 6 June 1791 created The Company and Proprietors of the Neath Canal Navigation, which sold shares to raise £25,000 with the ability to raise another £10,000 if needed. Thomas Dadford was the Engineer and by 1792 the canal had reached Ynysbwllog. Dadford resigned to work on another canal and was replaced by Thomas Sheasby, He was unable to finish the work by the time stipulated (November 1793) and was arrested in 1794 for fraud. The canal company had completed the building work by 1795.

A second Neath Canal Act was passed on 26 May 1798 permitting the building of an extension of two and a half miles to Giants Grave. Thomas Dadford was back at work surveying the route and Edward Price from Gofilon was the engineer. Lord Vernon financed the venture, which included nineteen locks and tramways. It was completed on 29 July 1799 at a cost of about £40,000. Between 1815 and 1842 additional docks and wharves were built at Giants Grave and in 1832 the canal was extended to Briton Ferry by the building of the Jersey Canal. This was built by the Earl of Jersey. Another extension was built in 1842.

The Maesmarchog branch was opened in 1800, the Aberclwyd branch in 1817, and there was another short branch at Court Sart.

The Tennant Canal was originally part of the Glan-y-wern Canal, which was built across Crymlyn Bog to transport coal to Red Jacket Pill. It was closed after twenty years, but in 1818 George Tennant, the son of a Lancashire solicitor, with no previous experience in canal-building, extended it to link the Neath to the Tawe at Swansea docks. Work began in 1817 and completed in the autumn of 1818. This canal ran from near the east pier on the River Tawe at Swansea to the Neath at Red Jacket.

An extension to the Aberdulais basin was built where it joined the Neath Canal, but because the requisite Act of Parliament had not been passed Tennant suffered a long delay before coming to an agreement with a landowner over the intended canal route. In April 1821 L. W. Dillwyn refused permission to allow Tennant to cut through his land to pass under the Swansea road. Eventually both men came to an agreement, but not before Dillwyn had described his adversary as a 'terrible plague'. Almost uniquely for a canal-owner, George Tennant purchased the land each side of the canal and so retained complete control. Once the canal was operating, much of the Neath traffic used the Tennant Canal, as Swansea provided better facilities for transferring cargo to ships.

The Tennant Canal carried about 90,000 tons a year, including coal, timber, iron ore, sand, slag and copper ore for Charles Lambert's copper works. In common with other canals, the railway (the Vale of Neath Railway in particular) proved stiff competition. By 1921 traffic on the canal had almost disappeared and it became redundant; today it is being restored to its former glory.

The Neath and Tennant canals were not used for trade after the 1930s, but because they supplied water to local industries and to Swansea docks they were kept open as water channels.

The term 'metropolis' given to a very large city or urban area comes from the Greek '*metros*' (mother) and '*polis*' (city). Many words end in '-*polis*', such as Tripolis (a group of three cities), Heliopolis (sun city), Necropolis (city of the dead). It was later used to describe a city regarded as a centre of a specified activity or any large, important city It may also refer to a special kind of city, such as Technopolis (a city with high-tech industry), or Cottonopolis (a name used for Manchester during the nineteenth entury when it was a major industrial centre for cotton spinning).

In the late eighteenth and early nineteenth centuries, Swansea, and its surrounding area, became known as 'Copperopolis', due to the fact that it dominated the world copper industry.

From autumn 1584 – the time of the first copper smelting in Neath, south Wales – up to 1820, Swansea became the most important early heavy industry centre in Wales, with 90 per cent of all copper smelting and metal manufacturing in Britain taking place within twenty miles of the city, on a 100-acre site. Up to 60 per cent of the world's copper was produced in Swansea, including all the Admiralty's requirements for sheathing the hulls of the Royal Navy's warships.

Possibly the first company to start working in the area was the Lockwoods company, which was founded by Richard Lockwood, a London merchant. Together with Swansea businessman Robert Morris, he formed Lockwood, Morris and Co. at the Llangynfelach works in 1727. When Lockwoods moved from Landore, they set up another smelter at Forest. The Harfords & Bristol Brass & Copper Company bought it in 1790 and it remained there until the company ceased to exist in 1833.

At about the same time the Old Copper Works at Burlais Brook junction with the Tawe were built by James Griffiths and other Quaker business partners in 1720. Griffiths & Co. bought a 50 per cent share of an Irish copper mine at Ballymurtagh, County Wicklow, in 1720 to ensure a supply of copper ore to the works, but like the Cambrian Works at Llanelli, the Old Copper Works was destined to become a pottery of sorts.

In a *Guide to Swansea*, written in 1802, the White Rock Copper Works at Pentrechwyth is described as a barren spot due to the sulphurous influence of other copper works. It is on a site that felt the shock of the 'Great Earthquake' that rocked the Swansea area on 1 November 1755. There is some doubt as to when and by whom the White Rock Copper Works at Pentrechwyth was built. It could have been in 1720 by Percival of Bristol. Others say that it was in 1737 by John Hoblyn. The works were operated by Thomas Coster and Company. Coster was an MP, a mine adventurer, and a dealer in brass and copper. The family were also partners with some of the slave houses of Bristol, and copper was very important as a form of currency to the slave market. The company was renamed in 1739 as Joseph Percivall and Copper Company. They operated the works until 1764 when the company was re-formed as John Freeman and Copper Company. From 1870 the works processed lead and silver, and was operated by Williams, Foster and Company and Vivian and Sons until 1874, then Vivian and Sons from 1874 until 1924, and British Copper Manufacturers' Limited 1924 until 1928.

In 2011 the significance of the White Rock Copper Works was demonstrated when it was chosen as one of a *100 Places that Made Britain* by Professor Chris Evans of the University of Glamorgan. The Forest Works was built sometime before 1740 by Morris Lockwood & Co. In 1775 there were twenty-one smelting furnaces, two refineries and eleven calciners in operation, producing 473 tons of copper a year.

Middle Bank or Plas Canol Copper Works, in the Lower Swansea Valley, originally worked lead under the firm of

Chauncey Townsend and Company, from 1755 until 1764. A clause in the lease for the works demanded that the copper works had to:

> burn and use such coals as shall be raised under the lands of ... Lousia Barbara Mansell only, and no other coals, so long as coals can be raised from the said Louisa Barbara Mansell's lands, in the parish of Llansamlet.'[4]

To accept such a clause was to put your head in a noose, but there was no choice as so much coal was needed for smelting. Having a supply of coal close to the works was of paramount importance and being able to convey it easily from the mine was a determining factor in the siting of any copper works. The Crown Copper Works at Giant's Leap was close to the Neath Canal; the Red Jacket and Briton Ferry works close to the Tennant Canal; Upper and Middle Bank and the White Rose close to the Smith Canal; Hafod, Morfa, Landore, Rose, Birmingham, Forest copper works close to the Swansea canal and the Tawe. Others were right on the doorstep of a colliery, such as Neath Abbey, Margam, Penclawdd, Spitty, Llanelly and Pembrey.

When John Rotton and Company took over the works (1765–1769) copper working was introduced.

Upper Bank Works opened in 1757. This was another lead works originally, but then was taken over by Thomas Williams, and from 1803 run jointly with his son Owen Williams and Pascoe Grenfell. By 1825, both the Upper and Middle Bank works were owned by the Grenfell family. It was here that George F. Muntz invented Muntz or Yellow Metal, which was used in the sheathing of ships and in the making of bolts and ship's brass.

The Birmingham Copper Works (1791) and the Rose Copper Works (1795) were both owned by a Birmingham company, possibly the Birmingham Mining and Copper Company. Over time they were both sold to other companies: Williams & Vivian and Grenfell, Williams & Fox and almost every other famous family name connected with the Swansea Copper Industry, like Fox, Foster, Bath and Nevill.

The Hafod Copperworks was built by John Vivian in 1810 on a site between the Swansea canal and the river Tawe. An anonymous poet described it as:

> Delightful Hafod, most serene abode!
> Thou sweet retreat, fit mansion for a god!
> Dame Nature, lavish of her gifts we see,
> And Paradise again restored in thee.[5]

S. C. Ganwell, in a District Guide said, 143 years later:

> Landore. A spot rich in the renown of its metal and chemical works, but to the casual visitor, ugly with all the ugliness of grime, and dust, and mud, and smoke and indescribable tastes and odours.[6]

How things had changed!

Hafod was the most modern works of its kind in Europe, and the largest, with thirty-six furnaces in 1819. John Vivian was partly educated in Germany and maintained many connections and friendships there. German scientists were invited to work and study at Hafod. In 1886 a thousand people were employed there manufacturing copper bars, bolts, circles, condenser plates, ingots, rods, sheets, sulphate of copper, tube and yellow metal as well as brass for naval use, ferro-bronze, gold, lead ingots, silver, spelter, sulphuric acid, superphosphate fertilisers and zinc chloride. Any new development was sure to be studied and used at Hafod. It was here that Gerstenhofer furnaces were used to convert the sulphurous smoke into sulphuric acid. Such was their efficiency that they replaced almost all the old-style furnaces.

The Vivian family had many irons in the fire, and the Hafod industrial complex included the Hafod Phosphate Works, Hafod Foundry, Hafod Forge and the Hafod Isaf Nickel & Cobalt Works. They also owned works at Landore, Morriston and White Rock.

Every worker had to come to an agreement with J. H. Vivian: for example, on 26 July 1811 William Howell signed an agreement with J. H. Vivian for the exclusive service of the former as a refiner or smelter of copper. This was to be for a period of twenty-one years, and no disclosures of the art or mystery of smelting or refining of copper were to be made except to William Howell's own children. In return for this he was to receive a weekly salary of 30s. plus 2 lb of candles plus a wey of coal (a wey is a measure of weight depending on the commodity – if coal, about 5 tons), plus £10 10s in lieu of a house and garden.

After 1894 the Vivians lost interest in the Hafod Copper works and in 1924 the firm became part of the Morfa complex, which was ironic as at the time of their founding, workers from the two works were separated by a high wall and were not allowed to talk to each other in case secrets were let out of the bag! They employed some 620 workers, with 120 furnaces for copper and zinc.

The latter was the largest non-ferrous metal smelter in the world by the mid-nineteenth century. British Copper Manufacturers owned the combined works until 1928, when they were taken over by ICI, although the refining of copper had ended around 1924. In 1957 the site was taken over by Yorkshire Imperial Metals, an amalgamation of ICI and Yorkshire Metals, and the two works functioned as one until closure in August 1980.

Nant-rhyd-y-vilais was founded by Messrs. Bevan of Morriston in 1814. At the works, they had air furnaces that could be used for smelting copper or iron. It was hoped to extract copper and iron from slag, and they were able to do so, but the iron obtained would not weld. The smelting that did take place was called a 'scientific success', but was not a commercial one, so their efforts were greatly curtailed; as a result, 'the proprietors came to grief, the works closed.'[7]

Morfa Copper Works, Landore [*Glandŵr*], was built on fifteen acres of land leased by the Duke of Beaufort to Williams, Foster and Company, made up of the Williams brothers (John, Michael and William) from Cornwall, and the Fosters (a Middlesex merchant family – Sampson and Joseph Talwin), on 5 December 1831. Rolling mills (1828) and a silver works (1840) were added to the site. In 1880 the works was acquired briefly by H. R. Merton and Company but were, in the same year, obtained by Williams, Foster and Company who ran them from 1890 to 1893. From 1893 until 1924 the works were operated by Williams, Foster and Company and Pascoe Grenfell and Sons Limited.

The 1850s and 60s saw what could be regarded as the final 'push for glory' in and around the Swansea copper Industry. The Port Tennant works was built in 1852 by Charles Lambert, who had other business interests in Chilean mines and smelting works. Port Tenant's works had to be destroyed when the east side of the Swansea docks was built.

In the same year James Stephens bought a small concern at Black Vale, Cwmbwrla. It was extended when smelters were built.

One almost forgotten by-line of the copper industry was extracting arsenic from copper ore. Another by-line was the extraction of sulphur. This happened at the Danygraig Works, built in 1860 by a Mr Jennings, who had transferred from the Clyne Wood Arsenic and Chemical Works. Williams, Foster & Company tried to buy the works but the sale was cancelled when J. M. Williams complained about a clause in the lease that stipulated that an extra £10 per annum had to be paid for every furnace built. A Mr Hadland stepped in to save the works from closure. (No more than this is known about either Mr Jennings or Mr Hadland.)

In 1862 two other copper works were established. One, owned by the Landore Arsenic and Copper Company was near to the Landore Works but on a much smaller scale and was known as the Little Landore Copper Works. The other was on the banks of the Smith Canal and built for convenience by the Swansea Vale Railway at Llansamlet. Mr Jennings of Danygraig put money into this venture to smelt ores rich in arsenic and sulphur.

When writing about all the above mentioned works in 1867 Grant Francis expressed a wish that 'this trade exist and long continue to flourish ... so that 'One and All' may alike rejoice, and with earnest vice, cry GOD SPEED THE COPPER TRADE'.[8] Little did he know that even then it was showing the first signs of a great change, and that by 1869 he would be admitting that 'the days of the copper trade are numbered'.[9]

---

[1] *Walk through South Wales, an account of a tour made in October 1819.* William and Sampson Sandys.

[2] *King Copper – South Wales and the Copper Trade 1584-1895.* Ronald Rees. (UWP, 2000).

[3] *Ibid.*

[4] *The Smelting of Copper in the Swansea District of South Wales from the Time of Queen Elizabeth to the Present Day.* Grant Francis. (Henry Sotheran & Co, 1881).

[5] *A Short History of the Hafod Copperworks 1810–1924.* Anonymous poet (1737).

[6] Swansea District Guide. S. C. Ganwell. *A Short History of the Hafod Copperworks 1810–1924.*

[7] Grant Francis, *op. cit.,* 1881.

[8] Grant Francis, *op. cit.,* 1881.

[9] Grant Francis, *op. cit.,* 1881.

11

Swansea copper barons

Due to their influence and fortunes, many an industrialist has been called a 'baron' – the lowest rank in the peerage. Of the leading copper industrialists in the Swansea area, possibly only one had the right to such a title as he had been created the first Baron Swansea. Henry Vivian Hussey was granted that honour in 1883. Another title, and possibly a much more suitable one, would be 'copper master', as a master, according to *The Concise English Dictionary* (1909), is 'one who directs; one who has others under his immediate control; an employer; the owner; proprietor; a man eminently skilled'.

- **Robert Morris** (d.1768) was a 'Shropshire lad', son of Robert Morris of Bishop's Castle. After a period in business in north Wales, where he married Margaret Jenkins of Machynlleth, the family moved to Tredegar. He arrived in south Wales in 1724 to manage the Llangyfelach Copper Works. In 1727 he went into partnership with Richard Lockwood and Edward Gibbon to form Morris Lockwood & Co. In June of that year, he travelled to Cornwall to buy a quantity of copper ore. He made a profit of almost £2,000 on his purchase and used the money to good use for his future business ventures. After a very fruitful period in copper smelting and coal mining (Llangyfelach Works 1726–1748; Cambrian Works 1735–1745; Forest Works and Forest Battery Works 1746–1793; Landore Works from 1793 (which he had acquired from Dr Lane of Bristol in payment of a debt); the partnership was dissolved in 1800.

The Morris family lived at Clasemont. Robert's daughter Bridget married into the Lockwood family. In his will, written on 28 May 1768, Robert Morris stated that he wished to be buried in Swansea in the church of St John (now St Matthews'). He bequeathed his estate to his second son John Morris.

- **Sir John Morris** (1745–1819) lived at Sketty Park and was made a baronet in 1806. His best remembered contribution is that he bore more responsibility than anyone else for the building of Morriston copper village.

- **Chauncy Townsend** (1708–1770) was a businessman who started as a London linen draper but extended his interests into coal mining, copper and lead smelting and refining in Swansea. Most of his money he ploughed into the mining business. From 1744 he was a government contractor with responsibility for supplying the military and settlers in Nova Scotia, Canada. He has been called the founder of the first industrial dynasty in south Wales by P. R. Reynolds. He was MP for Westbury, Wiltshire, between 1748 and 1768, and for Wigtown Burghs from 1768 until his death in 1770 – only the second Englishman ever chosen to represent a Scottish constituency – though once there, he never spoke in the House of Commons.

- **John Vivian** (1750–1826) cannot be ignored. Even though he was not originally from Swansea, as he was the founding member of a very important Swansea dynasty. He was the son of the vicar of Truro, and married Betsy Cranch, daughter of the vicar of St. Clements, near Truro. Little is known of his early life, but he became a renowned businessman with many interests in the copper industry. In 1800 he became a partner in the Penclawdd Smelting Works and by 1809 he had established his own works at Hafod, Swansea and had formed a new company: Vivian & Sons. He owned 50 per cent of the shares in the company himself and had given 25 per cent each to his two eldest sons Richard Hussey Vivian and John Henry Vivian. It was his dearest wish to have other sons to help in the business- 'one for Cornwall, one for London, one for Liverpool',[1] but he had to make do with employed agents. His third and youngest son Thomas died aged twenty one in 1821. There was one daughter, Lucy. John Vivian died following a hunting accident.

- **John Henry Vivian** (1785–1855) was the son of John Vivian, of Truro, Cornwall, who brought his business and expertise from Cornwall to south Wales. John Henry was sent to Germany in 1801 to study languages, and by 1803 was at the University of Freiburg in the Black Forest studying mineralogy, geology, chemistry, metallurgy and mathematics. He returned to Britain in 1804 to join the family business and by 1811 he had been appointed manager of the Hafod Works, where he was aware of the problems caused by the smoke from the works and worked to eliminate them. John Henry had many business interests mainly in the copper industry in Swansea, Liverpool, Birmingham and London, and at the same time pursued other interests as well. Between 1832 and 1855 he was Member of Parliament for Swansea. He was also a Justice of the Peace; the Deputy Lieutenant of the county; a major in the Royal Stannary Artillery, as well as a Fellow of the Royal Society, a member of the Geological Association, a founder member in 1835 of the Philosophical and Literary Society (later the Royal Institution of South Wales) and a founder member in 1846 of the Cambrian Archaeological Association.

After his marriage to Sarah, the eldest daughter of Arthur Jones of Reigate, on 30 October 1816, the couple lived at Marino, Swansea. They had eight children. He suffered many bouts of illness but was known, despite the problems, as a hard worker. All his employees were expected to keep to his standards and it was only in 1840 that he agreed to allow the men to work 12-hour rather than 24-hour shifts. He was a shy character and kept himself to himself rather than mix with other coppermasters.

In 1829, the Vivian family moved to the forty-two acre Singletons Farm. Later, it was re-named as Singleton Abbey and the farm became the home farm for the estate. In 1920 Singleton Abbey became part of Swansea University and now houses the University's administration block. He died on 10 February 1855 and will always be remembered as a Swansea man 'through and through'. It was due to his leadership that Swansea developed in the way it did. His wife lived for another thirty-one years after him. She died on 8 September 1886.

- **Henry Hussey Vivian**, 1st Baron Swansea (1821–1894), was the eldest son of John Henry Vivian. After an Eton education he was sent to France, where he lodged in the same house in Le Havre as Friedrich Engles, and Germany to study metallurgy in 1838 before being accepted at Trinity College, Cambridge in 1840. He became manager of the Liverpool branch of the family business in 1842 and was later a partner in the firm after which he was made manager of the Hafod Copper Works in 1845. His knowledge of the industry led him to develop a number of by-products from copper smelting, and he took out a number of patents in connection with the manufacture of spelter, gold, silver, nickel and cobalt. It was also his decision in 1860 to use the Moritz Gerstenhöffer process to smelt copper, so as to reduce the amount of smoke produced by other less efficient methods.

The 'sliding scale' of miners' wages was one of his ideas after a period of industrial unrest in 1889. To facilitate his copper works, he was one of the chief promoters of the Rhondda and Swansea Bay Railways and helped to develop and extend the harbour facilities in Swansea.

On 15 April 1847 he married Jessie Dalrymple Goddard (c.1825–1848), daughter of Ambrose Goddard, Swindon. Sadly, his wife died a few weeks after the birth of their only child, Ernest Ambrose Vivian, 2nd Baron Swansea (1848–1922). Sadly for the family, Ernest had no interest in the copper industry business.

Veranda House, Singleton Park, Swansea, had been purchased by John Henry Vivian in 1847 for his son Henry and and his wife, but after Jessie's death Henry could not live in the house by himself.

On 14 July 1853 he married his second wife, Lady Flora Caroline Elizabeth Cholmeley (d. 1868), daughter of Sir Montague Cholmeley, 2nd Baronet. They had one son, John Aubrey Vivian (1854–1898). Despite suffering from major health problems such as epilepsy, John Aubrey had a little business acumen, but his life was cut short.

Lord Swansea married his third wife, Averil

Beaumont (1841–1934), daughter of Capt. Richard Beaumont, R.N. on 10 November 1870. They had six children.

From 1852 to 1857 Henry Hussey Vivian was Liberal Member of Parliament for Truro, from 1857 to 1885 for Glamorgan, and from 1885 to 1893 he was the member for Swansea District. He was also a Justice of the Peace, Deputy Lieutenant for Glamorgan and a Lieutenant-Colonel of the 4th Glamorgan Rifle Volunteers. On 13 May 1882 he was created a baronet and on 9 June 1893 became Baron Swansea. Only hours after his return home from a visit to the United States of America he died at Singleton Abbey on 24 November 1894 and was buried in Sketty churchyard.

- **Arthur Pendarves Vivian** (1834–1924) was educated at Freiburg University and by 1855 was in charge of the Margam Copper Works. He married in 1867. Despite being the chairman of Vivian & Sons after the death of William Graham Vivian in 1912 and retaining his post as manager of Margam Copper Works until 1913, he was not, unlike other members of his family, very interested in the copper industry and much preferred to spend time in Cornwall.

- **Richard Glynn Vivian** (1835–1910) was the fourth son of John Henry Vivian. From his father's estate he inherited a quarter-share in Vivian & Sons but was not inclined to be involved in the copper or metal industry. He preferred to concentrate on the arts and foreign travel. His collection of paintings and china were offered to Swansea in 1905, and the Glynn Vivian Gallery was opened in July 1911.

- **Pascoe Grenfell** (1761–1838) was a businessman and a politician. His roots were in Cornwall: he was born and baptized at Marazion, the son of a tin and copper merchant. He was educated at Truro Grammar School and was then sent to Amsterdam to learn the business of banking. Later, he joined his father and uncle in business in London. After a period of working with Thomas Williams, the Copper King, he was appointed manager of the works at Holywell and was later a partner in the firm of Williams & Grenfell. Grenfell went into a partnership with Owen Williams (Thomas Williams' son) in 1794 to buy Cornish copper ore for the Middle and Upper Bank Copper Works in Swansea, which lasted until 1829. When the partners separated, Grenfell set up his own family business of Pascoe Grenfell & Sons. From 1829 to 1830 he was also Governor of the Royal Exchange Assurance Company.

Grenfell lived in Taplow House, Great Marlow, Buckinghamshire, and followed Williams as MP for Great Marlow for eighteen years (1802–1820), after which he represented Penryn, Cornwall, until June 1826. He was a strong supporter of William Wilberforce in Parliament.

As he lay dying in London he was described as 'our beloved master and friend'[2] by his workforce in south Wales. After his death on 23 January 1838 it was the same workforce who helped pay for a memorial window to be placed at Kilvey church.

- **Pascoe St Leger Grenfell** (1798–1879) was a member of one of the leading copper smelting families of the nineteenth century. He was the second son of Pascoe Grenfell and was christened at St Martin-in-the-Fields, London, on 15 January 1799. After being educated at Eton College and in France, he joined the family business in Swansea who, at the beginning of the century, had a controlling interest in the Middle and Upper Banks copper works.

Pascoe St Leger followed his brother Riversdale to Swansea and in 1844 was manager of the company. He was a very reasonable employer and chose to live in Maesteg House in the eastern area of the town, where many of his workers lived, and suffer the same discomfort from the smoke as they did.

All Saints Church, Kilvey, was built by him and his family; he was a Sunday school teacher there for thirty years. He also built the Kilvey 'ragged schools', a concert hall and other buildings for the use of the community. He was Chairman, then Treasurer, of the Swansea Harbour Trust, a Borough Councillor, Justice of the Peace and Deputy-Lieutenant of the County of Glamorgan. He was a member of the Committee of the Swansea Board of Health.

- **Dr John Lane** (1678–1741) was a scientific man, a doctor and a metallurgist. He was educated at Exeter College, Oxford, and studied medicine at Leyden in 1702. Lane and his stepfather-in-law John Pollard became partners of Thomas Collins at the Neath Abbey Copper Works in 1694, but the partnership was dissolved in 1716, only for Lane and Pollard to establish the Llangyfelach Copper Works at Landore in 1717. It was made bankrupt in 1726. Dr Lane's other ventures kept him in Bristol; despite his company being bankrupted, his reputation was sound.

- **Humphrey Mackworth** (1657–1727) is remembered as an industrialist and a parliamentarian and was the son of Thomas and Ann Mackworth, of Bretton Grange, Shropshire. He was called to the Bar in 1682 and was knighted by Charles II on 15 January

1683 when he was twenty-eight years old.

His wife Mary, whom he married on 16 June 1686, was the daughter of Sir Herbert Evans, Gnoll, Neath, and was from a family of mine owners. The leases they held on different mines were renewed for Humphrey on his marriage, and on his wife's death in 1696 he inherited all her estate. Due to the fact that local coal was being used for smelting in Neath, Humphrey became interested in copper smelting. He became the owner of copper and lead/silver mines in Cardiganshire, and in 1694 bought Sir Carbery Pryse's interests for £16,440. Matters did not go well in Neath, and after many disputes with Sir Edward Mansel of Briton Ferry and others, Mackworth was declared bankrupt on 1709. He was found guilty of dubious practices by a House of Commons committee in 1710, but due to a change of government in that year he was saved, and rose again to form the Company of Mineral Manufacturers in 1713. His empire grew steadily and he bought land and houses in Neath to become one of the leaders of society in the town.

In 1701 Mackworth was elected Member of Parliament for Cardiganshire, and was re-elected from 1710 to 1713. Once in Parliament he was a very active member and served on many committees.

On 8 March 1699 he became one of the founding members of the Society for Propagation of Christian Knowledge. In 1706 his company paid £20 a year towards a Charity School at the Esgair Hir mine in Cardiganshire and £30 pounds to pay for a minister in the same area, as well as £20 for a charity school in Neath. As there were difficulties in appointing a teacher in Neath, Mackworth suggested using a 'travelling master' to start new schools and move on to another area afterwards.

Humphrey Mackworth was a driven man. He built canals and quays, docks, and tramlines for sail-driven trams, which enabled a horse to do the work of ten and a man to do the work of twenty. The trams were intended to carry coal to the smelting furnaces and to the port. He brought in workers from Shropshire and Derbyshire, even from Germany, and when he had need of them he would employ condemned pirates, and prisoners who had been pardoned. He set them a condition that they would be apprenticed to his company for at least five years. From his workers he demanded complete loyalty. All of them had to work for his company for at least twelve months, with the advantage that they could not be press-ganged to the Navy at a time of war. In 1700 he asked for condemned prisoners from Norfolk to join his workforce at Neath. Seven took advantage of his offer, but the people of Neath were not best pleased.

- **R. J. Nevill** (d.1856) was a very keen businessman and managing partner of the Llanelli Copper Works. In 1818 he was manager of General Warde's three collieries near Llanelli and in 1829 he became the owner, as the general could not pay his debt of almost £30,000 to Nevill. Three years earlier,he had gained control of the collieries of Alexander Raby in similar circumstances.

Nevill won a Government contract in 1833 to supply 500 tons of coal to the West Indies. Llanelli harbour was not big enough to for a ship to carry the load, so he arranged for the coal to be put on smaller ships, taken to Bristol and re-loaded into a bigger vessel, despite the risk of the large lumps of coal being broken into much smaller ones, which the contract specified that it did not want.

His funeral was one of the largest ever seen in the town and was described as one of 'enormous proportions'.[3]

[1] *Singleton Abbey and the Vivians of Swansea.* R. A. Griffiths. (Gomer, 1988).

[2] *King Copper: South Wales and the Copper Trade 1584–1895. Ronald Rees.* (University of Wales Press, 2000).

[3] *Ibid.*

12

Copper towns and villages

Some towns and villages are known for their connections or products associated with them. Llannerch-y-medd, Anglesey, was known as the village of cobblers producing clogs for the miners at Parys Mountain. Nefyn, a fishing village on Llŷn peninsula, was famous for its herrings. Dowlais was an 'iron' town, whilst Treorchy and Ferndale were 'coal' towns.

Other villages and towns came into being because of the copper works. Amlwch and Amlwch Port were nondescript places until the copper works on Parys Mountain helped develop one as a town and the other as a harbour. Today both have slipped back into a 'post-copper-works slumber', as have other towns and villages in south Wales.

All copper towns and villages were built near the works so as to convenience the workers as much as possible. Such places did not have the best of reputations. Taibach was said by Edward Donovan in 1804 to have a dirty appearance and inhabitants, but the famous Constantinople Row of Taibach was a row of whitewashed cottages so sparkling in the sun that they served as a landmark for sailors. Trevivian or Hafod was described as insanitary, overcrowded and ugly in 1840. Of consolation to the inhabitants was the fact that they were considered better than coal towns! One visitor to Wales, Sophia Ward, said in 1791 that she thought that the lower class of people had better habitation and she was pleased to note that they usually had geraniums at their windows.[1]

Generally, houses of such places were badly ventilated, had no running water or drains, and were damp. Out the back were the usual ash heap, pigsty, rubbish dump, and an outside toilet at the bottom of what little garden there was.

Between 1768 and 1774 John Morris, owner of the Forest Works, commissioned the first purpose-built block of flats or tenements in Britain, with room for forty families, off Trewyddfa Road, Llandore in Swansea. The first families to move in paid the first rent instalment on 29 August 1773. With its four-storey towered corners, battlements of blocks of shaped copper slag and three-storey interconnecting blocks, it was called Morris Castle. This was one of the first high-rise buildings in the area. In its day, this was a modern building which had amenities such as central heating, with each floor being heated from the floor below, and a central rubbish disposal system. Outside were a central courtyard, gardens and a potato patch for each of the families. One of the main drawbacks of the building was that it did not have a constant supply of fresh water, as it was sited so high up above the valley. Despite such services it was a place where few actually liked living. Getting to and going from there involved a long hard climb, usually carrying a bucket of water. Morris was known as a man concerned about his workers' welfare, to such an extent that he housed a tailor and a shoemaker in Morris Castle. He put the castle up for sale in 1811 but found no takers. It was occupied until 1850 but local opencast coal mining at Cnap Llwyd made it unsafe. By 1880 it was in ruins. On 25 January 1990 the easternmost wall of the building collapsed in high winds.

Another of Morris' projects was the much bigger village of Morris Town, today known as Morriston, about four miles north of Swansea on the west bank of the Tawe. This was a model town, designed by Caerphilly-born William Edwards, bridge-builder (Wychtree Bridge, 1778; Pontypridd Old Bridge – at one time the longest single-span bridge in the world), chapel-builder (Libanus Chapel, 1782), engineer and preacher. The site chosen for Morris

Town was north of the Forest Copper Works on the banks of Nant Felin, a mill stream renowned for trout. Morriston is a fine example of early town planning and had a rectangular pattern of straight, wide streets with a main square where the two main streets crossed. The main street was called Edward Street but was later changed to Morfydd Street. Morris' idea was that the workers would lease a plot of land a quarter of an acre in size to build on, for a period of fifty-five years at 7/6 per year and a small rent. All the houses were to be detached, two storeys high, with a central doorway and whitewashed front, each with its own garden, facing the river. This was supposed to produce a village atmosphere and a sense of community. To further encourage that some people were allowed to keep a cow on the Trewyddfa Common.

Building began in 1790 using local masons and local stone. By 1796, 141 houses had been erected with a total of 619 residents (an average of four per house). There was also land allocated for two chapels and poorhouses, sited in Morriston and Sketty. Another scheme for the benefit of the residents was the setting up of a Compensation Fund for the workers in case of injury, sickness and old age. By 1819 almost 300 stone cottages with tiled roofs had been built in the village.

Despite sounding an ideal place to live, problems had to be faced. The streets were poorly surfaced and not cleaned. Lighting and ventilation in the houses were not satisfactory and no provisions for drainage had been included in the plans. Drinking water supplies were often contaminated by sewage. Despite its shortcomings, to many it proved an acceptable place to live and work and the population grew from 3,000 in 1832 to 7,302 in 1851.

When the copper industry waned in the 1850s the tinplate industry grew; Morriston became known as the town of tinplate workers. Another sign of changing times was when the last horse-drawn tram from Swansea to Morriston made the journey on 30 June 1900. The times were changing with the century.

When the Grenfell family took over from the Nevill family at Llanelli, they rented out eighty specially built two-up, two-down houses on Kilvey Hill at 6d. per room. They had no water supply but were considered better than most other available houses.

The Vivian family bought the English Copper Company in 1837 and needed 130 houses for their Taibach workers. At Hafod they built houses for their key workers and by 1845 owned sixty cottages forming two streets. These were of a simple design – two-up, two-down, back-to-back, in terraces named after Vivian family members such as Glynn, Graham, Odo and Vivian. The largest dwellings had a kitchen, downstairs passage and parlour, with three upstairs bedrooms for parents, sons and daughters. Outside were a coal hole, garden, pigsty and toilet. All roads and pavements were properly laid and surfaced. Until 1850 there was no water supply to the houses, except for the larger ones; but even though there were no drains the houses were in much better condition than those in Pentrechwith on the north side of Trevivian or Hafod, where the houses were damp and dirty and squeezed into a niche in the hillside. Seeping toilets and rubbish heaps polluted the springs and wells at Trevivian at the bottom of the hill.

The Vivians were much praised by George T. Clark, local commissioner of the General Board of Health, and Dr Thomas Williams, Swansea physician, for their provision for the workers. These included many Irish workers, who glorified in their homes, which were of a much better standard than what most of them had endured at home. They, who were regarded as the poorest of the poor, appreciated the togetherness afforded them in such circumstances, as it meant that they could keep their culture and language alive. Many other families from a rural Welsh-speaking background appreciated the same togetherness, as it meant that relatives were close by and many a son followed his father or uncle to the copper works. Morriston was regarded as a warm and friendly town, while Swansea was considered to be full of frigid, snobbish and more anglicised people. Swansea, a more cosmopolitan place, was like a foreign country to many of those who had come from elsewhere in Wales.

Cwmafan Valley is only three miles long and a mile wide. In 1801 the population of the parish was only 232, but when the heavy industries of coal, copper, iron and tinplate congregated in the valley the population grew to over 4,000 by 1841. One of the 'Glamorgan Wonders' was built on the summit of Mynydd y Foel. This was a 43-foot-high stack linked by a tunnel to the copper works in the valley below, to carry fumes and smoke from the village and its environs. The metal contents of the fumes would collect on the tunnel walls and would be scraped off and re-used. Long after the copper works closed the stack remained. It was demolished in 1940, as it was thought it would be a landmark for German bombers during the Second World War.

Iron ore deposits were found on the Foel and Mynydd y Gaer in the 1810s, resulting in the opening of mines and two smelting furnaces. Developing the works proved costly and the owner was forced to leave in 1819. Two Cornishmen came to revitalise the works and the valley: John Vigurs and Leonard Smith. Their partnership did not last long, and in 1835 Vigurs established the Vigurs Company. He built a copper works and a horse-drawn tramway to carry its produce down to Port Talbot Docks. The first consignment left Cwmafan in 1838. He made many improvements in and around the village, but he did not stay long in Wales and had returned to Cornwall by the end of the year.

The English Copper Company took over the copper works and built several hundred houses for its workers in the 1840s. All necessary services were included such as a market, mechanics' institute, reading room (with twenty and more newspapers and journals for those who took advantage of the service), savings bank, schools, shops and a company store (until they were disallowed by law in 1844). All the houses were two storeys high and back-to-back.

When the English Copper Company was declared bankrupt in 1848 the Bank of England insisted on installing a manager who was involved in almost all the village activities. He was the accountant John Biddulph, who became one of the most unpopular men in the village. He was appointed church warden at the Easter vestry of 5 April 1850. This was not 'a marriage made in Heaven'. Biddulph insisted that the local children attend church services and that they be caned if they did not. He also insisted that the Welsh language was not to be used in school. To his credit, he did become involved with the renovation of the Cwmafan church and raised the necessary money from the Governors of the Bank of England and the copper works directors. He disregarded the architect in charge of the renovations but did make use of the copper workers to work on the church when production was low. The Biddulph family donated a new Chancel East window, a communion set and seating in the Chancel and Nave of the new church when it was re-opened on Friday, 16 March 1851.

Biddulph, the villagers and his workers did not see eye to eye and due to much local opposition he and his family were forced to leave Cwmafan in 1852.

A report from The Post Office in 1871 gave much valuable information about Cwmafan:

Cwmafan is a populous hamlet, situated two miles from Port Talbot, and connected therewith by a railway, the property of the Governor and Company of Copper Miners in England, and is used by them for the transit of merchandise to and from the docks there. Nearly the whole of the hamlet is occupied by the iron, tin plate, and copper works and the collieries belonging to the Company. The smoke from these works is carried up a high mountain by a culvert to its summit at which point it terminates in a stack about fifty feet high, and on top of which is 1,200 feet above the level of the furnaces and 1,400 feet above the level of the sea. There are several schools here in connexion with the copper works, and the educational wants of the people are well cared for by the company. The Governor and Company of Copper Miners in England are lords of the manor and chief landowners.[2]

Whilst the workers were struggling with their daily grind, the gentry were comfortable in their palaces. Most of the 'byddigion' (well-to-do people/gentry) were living in the same areas but not quite as close to the works. They wanted to be clear of the smoke, so most of their houses were on the western side, taking advantage of the fresh air and the view. The Grenfells made the mistake of living 'in the smoke'. In 1830 Pascoe St Leger Grenfell built Maesteg House to be near to, but also upwind of, the Upper and Middle Bank Copper Works. To his credit, he stayed there until his death in 1879. Robert Morris also made the same mistake when he commissioned the architect John Johnson to plan and build Clasemont overlooking the Forest Works in Morriston. As it was sited downwind of the smoke, most of the surrounding plant life was killed. The house was later demolished and the family moved to a new house in Sketty, designed by William Jernegan, a Channel Islander and former assistant to John Johnson.

J. H. Vivian, after his marriage to Sarah Jones in 1816, bought a house on the coast, west of the town so as to be close to the Hafod Works. This was another house originally designed by William Jernegan. Built in 1783, it was an eight-sided house named Marino, where Edward King, the deputy controller and collector of HM Customs at Swansea port, lived. After buying the freehold for £2,887, in 1817 Vivian added two wings to the house to give it a more normal or usual shape, and had a replica American log cabin and a Swiss chalet-type cottage built in the grounds. Twenty years later he had it altered and redesigned by the architect and designer Peter Frederick Robinson and rebuilt in a Tudor style. In 1829 Vivian bought a forty-two acre farm owned by the Singletons. He renamed it as Singleton Abbey, although it has also been known as Singleton Hall, Park, and Lodge. Despite being known as Singleton Abbey it had, and has, never been an ecclesiastical building.

John Henry's wife Sarah was a keen gardener and had plants sent from the Himalayas and from India for her gardens. Another keen gardener was John Morris who had a Gothic-style greenhouse built at Sketty Park Mansion.

Graham Vivian lived at Woodlands, known as Clyne Castle after 1860. It was built in the Gothic style with exotic gardens surrounding the house. The fifty-room mansion was full of continental antiquities. He also bought all the surrounding properties so he could call himself the Squire of Blackpill.

Henry Hussey Vivian had two mansions to call home: Verandah and Park Wern. But on his mother's death he returned to Singleton. Park Wern was a castle-like house with towers and turrets, croquet lawns, grounds, gardens and vineries.

When Henry's wife Jessie died in 1848, her father-in-law built a church in her memory on the edge of the Singleton estate. Built of Cornish stone, it was consecrated by the Bishop of St. David's on 27 September 1850. The Vivian family were said to reign supreme in all matters industrial and spiritual in Swansea, Sketty and Hafod.

---

[1] *The Brighton of Wales. D. Boorman. (Swansea, 1986).*
[2] *The Post Office Directory 1871.*

13

'Now we are ready to head for the Horn'

Some nicknames are labels of contempt and derision; others are bestowed as labels of honour. To be called a 'Copper Ore Man' was certainly a label of honour, and to be labelled a 'Cape Horner' was a matter of honour and pride to Swansea sailors who had made the long voyage from Swansea across the Bay of Biscay and the Atlantic Ocean, crossing the Equator and then rounding Cape Horn through Drake's Passage and into the Pacific Ocean sailing for Chile, before returning home. Such was their own self-respect that when labelled a 'Cape Horner', all Swansea Jacks (a title given to Swansea sailors for their skill and dependability) when ashore in a foreign port could be instantly recognised as they were always smartly dressed, wearing a white braided cap and gold ear-rings. It is said that they tried to outdo one another by the smartness of their appearance.

Swansea had more Cape Horners than any other port in Britain because ships from south Wales' premier copper port undertook so many voyages to South America with cargoes of coal, and returning with copper ore or regulus. American sailors would say that it was of no use to go into any South American mineral exporting port as Swansea men had usually been there before them.

The first Swansea ships were small and probably built elsewhere, in such places as Cornwall and Devon. They carried their cargo of copper ore to be smelted in the Neath Valley. John Bwaple, in a 1585 document, has the honour of being the first named as captain of a copper-ore-carrying ship sailing into South Wales from Cornwall: 'John Bwaple, one of Wales, w' h his barc for a frayght of Copp' owre for

Wales , and did delyver hem ... 15 Tunn & 8 hundred of copp'owre.'[1] As so much coal was needed to smelt copper (30 tons of coal per 12 tons of ore to produce one ton of copper), and as Swansea was situated so close to a ready supply, small coastal vessels from Cornwall, Cardigan, Anglesey and even County Wicklow in Ireland sailed regularly to and fro.

The first ships built in Swansea had 'homely' names such as *Mary and Susannah, John and Sarah, William* etc. Weighing an average of 65 tons, they contributed to Swansea's growth by plying their trade of carrying ore to be smelted, and cargoes of much-needed everyday goods such as dairy products, meat, wool etc. On 11 June 1682 a Swansea ship arrived in Bridgwater, Somerset with a cargo of forty caldrons of coal (a caldron was a London measure: by a law of 1665, one caldron = 36 bushels, weighing 25 1/3 hundredweights, about 2837 pounds avoirdupois (about 1287 kilograms)); 20 gallons of butter; two bags of nails; sixty Welsh pigs and forty sheep.

On June 29th the *Thomas and Elizabeth*, a Neath ship, arrived at Bridgwater with 36 caldrons of coal, four dickers of leather, thirty-four half gallons of butter in pots, 200 bags of oatmeal, one bag of wool, five flitches of bacon, a thousand eggs, one piece gray flannel, one piece blanket, two dozen stockings and two gross Welsh gartering.

As the industry grew and trade increased, bigger ships were needed and built. Having to sail to foreign markets necessitated ocean-going vessels rather than the smaller coasters that had been so prevalent during the eighteenth century.

The first load of foreign ore, from Australia, arrived at the Hafod Works in 1827. Following that, ore from Cuba, South America and Spain was imported regularly, and by the 1830s copper mines in Chile and Peru were producing ore

Sketch map of important copper-mining sites in Chile

at full strength with Swansea ships carrying ever-increasing loads from South America. By the 1850s ships of 300 to 1,000 tons were sailing all over the globe from Swansea. A fleet of 150 ships were involved in 'CO-CH' voyages – 'Coal Out, Copper Home.' Ships and sailors that crossed the Atlantic were known as 'Copper Ore Men.'

To carry copper ore required a specially-designed ship, and copper ore barques were built for their strength in carrying an awkward cargo rather than for their speed. A broad bottom and a long body were the ideal requirements for such a ship, which would weigh, laden, about 3,000 to 5,000 tons.

A barque (or bark) was usually a three-masted vessel, the fore and main masts square-rigged and the mizzen mast or aftermast rigged fore and aft. More of this type was built than all other square rigs combined. A crew of about fifteen would sail them. As Swansea copper smelters paid relatively high wages, it was difficult to persuade Swansea men to sign on as crew members, so many of the crews were of a Welsh rural background who had left the hard work of farm labouring for an even harder and more dangerous life at sea. As the destinations became more exotic, international crew members were recruited.

Copper ore was a difficult cargo to carry. Holds were deep in the ship's body; masts were tall so the centre of gravity was low, which resulted in much rolling in poor weather. The cargo shifted easily in bad weather as the holds would not have been fully-filled because copper ore is quite dense and a small amount accounts for a lot of weight. In the 1850s special wooden containers or trunks were built, and tightly packed inside the holds, and the barques were known as 'Swansea-fitted' ships. With the stacked boxes, the centre of gravity was raised, which made for less rolling in dirty weather. It also meant that the ore was kept from bilge waters, so the danger of copper salts in the water eroding the copper bolts holding the ship's timbers together was eradicated. In case there had been any shift of the cargo, the ship's carpenter would go down into the hold every morning and evening to tighten up any shoring that had become loose through the movement of the ship.

Such barques were built in Barnstaple, Bideford, Llanelli, Swansea, Sunderland, and on Prince Edward Island, Canada. The main Canadian barque-builder was Swansea-born William Richards. William was born in 1819 and educated at Swansea and Waterford in Ireland. He went to sea with his father. By 1844, twenty-five year old William was master of the *John Hawkes*, a Prince Edward Island-built brig. In 1845 he met his future father-in-law James Yeo on the island, and married one of James' daughters in 1849. Until 1864 he built and captained ships in partnership with his father-in-law. His brother, Thomas Picton Richards, was a shipowner and broker in Swansea, and between 1859 and 1890 the brothers built more than ninety vessels on Prince Edward Island, mostly for British and Swansea owners.

One shipowner who dealt with the Richards Brothers was Henry Hoskins, a Cornishman. He moved to Swansea to operate copper ore ships, and between 1871 and 1876 bought six Prince Edward Island barques including the *Cyrus* (3/400 tons), the *Empress* and the *Cwm Donkin* (600 tons). Other ships that Hoskins owned were *Bride*, a 428-ton schooner, Swansea-built in 1872, which was lost in bad weather; *Bridegroom*, a 497-ton schooner, Swansea-built in 1874, which was abandoned due to a fire in the hold on a voyage between Liverpool and Valparaíso, though all crew members were saved; *Bridesmaid*, a 498-ton schooner, Swansea-built in 1875, and the *Gadlys*, which was lost after leaving Guayacan, Chile with a cargo of copper ore.

The maiden voyage of the Swansea-bound barques was to cross the Atlantic Ocean. On arrival the vessels would have their hulls strengthened and re-caulked, and deck-houses were constructed. Canadian pine had been used in the construction of such ships, but as it is considered to be softwood many alterations were needed for the voyages. Its best quality was that it was a very buoyant wood, which was very advantageous when carrying cumbersome, heavy cargoes.

Another Swansea connection with Cape Horn copper barques is that of the Bath family. One of Henry III's knights in 1217 was Sir Walter de Bath, Sheriff of Devon. A descendant of the sheriff was Henry Bath, born in Falmouth, Cornwall in 1776, who founded a copper trading business in 1794 when he was only eighteen years old. In 1822 the business moved to Bath's Copper Ore Yard, Bath Lane, Swansea. Henry Bath II was a partner, and Bath & Son owned a fleet of ships trading in the developing copper trade with Chile. Like most other ships in the same business it was 'Coal Out-Copper Home' for the fleet. Bath & Son was a very enterprising company, which soon became involved in all aspects of the trade, including ore sampling, weighing, setting freight and landing charges and selling by the Ticketing process.

Ticketing was an elaborate way of dealing, and the dictionary definition does not do justice to it. A wooden label was used to show where a particular pile of ore had come from, on what ship and on which date, how much was available, and what was its metal content.

Ticketing copper ore first occurred in Cornwall in 1728, with four companies involved, and was first held in Swansea in 1804. By 1815 it had become an important part of town life. The first Ticketing was held at the old Assembly Rooms but later moved to the Mackworth Hotel.

Buyers would place a sealed bid for the ore. Company owners would treat the buyers and sellers to a slap-up dinner, after which all the bids or tenders would be opened, and read aloud. Winning bidders would then arrange to transport the ore to be smelted. Newspapers published the winning bids and this established a national and world price for copper. This method of selling had the advantage of guaranteed sales and quick payment, but prices were determined by agreement rather than by competition. Sometimes a particular mine would sell their ore at a loss to ensure they could stay in business.

In 1846 Henry Bath II established the Swansea Iron Shipbuilding Company and in 1849 launched the steam yacht *Firefly*, to be used for sailing on the Chilean coast. Many of the company's ships, built at Bideford in Devon and Glasgow, were given Greek names or names from the novels of Fenimore Cooper. The fleet consisted of up to thirty barques. Another two vessels were named *Henry Bath* and *City of Valparaíso*. Almost all their ships were 'Cape Horners'.

When Henry Bath II and his brother Edward visited Chile they met and married daughters of Charles Lambert, a Swansea shipbuilder and copper merchant. With these marriages, Henry Bath & Co. became associated with the copper smelting business in Chile at Coquimbo, and at Port Tennant in Wales.

During the 1850s Henry II and another brother, Charles, a copper yard and fleet manager, opened a London office. In January 1877 the London Metal Exchange was formed and met at 4 Lombard Lane. Another office was opened in Liverpool. In 1890 the British Government passed a special Act of Parliament which gave Henry Bath & Sons the power to issue transferrable Certificates and Delivery Notes from their offices. This power was updated in 1910 and is still held by the company.

Another branch of the company's activities was ship-breaking, which began with the purchase of the *Great Eastern* in 1888. As copper imports dwindled, the company started buying and selling steel and is regarded today as a company with worldwide holdings and interests.

A natural development from building wooden sailing ships was to build iron ones. The first purpose-built iron sailing ship for the Chilean copper trade and the journey round Cape Horn was the 550-ton *La Serena*, built at the Neath Abbey Yard of John Tregelles Price in 1848. The later steam-powered ships proved to be unsuitable as there was no supply of coal or suitable berthing harbours in South America for them.

The first sizeable loads of foreign ore arrived in Swansea from Cuba. The Cobre mine in Cuba supplied the ore which was shipped from Santiago de Cuba. Cobre was originally mined by the Spanish but closed down, later to be re-opened in the 1830s by an Englishman. His twenty Cornish miners were unable to withstand the heat and other conditions and many died, only to be replaced by slaves from the Canary Islands and Cuba. The Cobre Company had its own wharf at Swansea known as the Cobre in the North Dock.

Chilean ore proved to be of a better quality than Cuban ore. The copper content of Cuban ore was twenty-five per cent compared to the Chilean content of up to 60 per cent. (Cornish ore had only a 6 to 8 per cent copper content.) Slowly, Chilean names such as Antofagasta, Carizal, Copiapo (which, due to the trapped miners, became a topic of conversation in Britain more than 180 years later), La Serena, at Coquimbo and Tocopilla were heard in conversations in Swansea. Ships from Swansea called at

Valparaíso for orders and then moved up or down the coast to load the ore, regulus or Chili bars (roughly smelted ore). Conditions at the Chilean mines were very hard. Men had to carry 200 pounds of copper ore up ladders to the surface and only if the mine was more than 600 feet deep were they allowed to rest on the way up.

Copper ore worth £1,000,000 was imported from South America to Swansea in 1861. In addition, Cuba supplied ore to the value of £150,000; Australia and other countries, £350,000 worth. This was the apogee of 'Copperopolis'.

Working conditions on the ships were hard. The crew had to unload the coal by transferring the hundredweight sacks into lighters by means of a sling. This work was done during twelve-hour shifts, and a cargo of 400 tons would take up to a fortnight to unload. Loading the copper ore for the return voyage was also back-breaking work. It was a slow and painful process, but when the last load of ore was lifted from the quayside onto the ship a sailor and a bottle of strong spirits would be on the hoist and the remaining crew members would join in the singing of 'Whisky for my Johnnie':

Whisky drove me around Cape Horn,
Whisky Johnnie.
It was many a month when I was gone,
Whisky for my Johnnie.[2]

The 15,000-mile trips to Chile and back could take up to six or even nine months. Ships had to cross the Doldrums, a very slow part of the voyage which could take weeks as favourable winds were very hard to find. Then they 'crossed the line' (the Equator) and went round Cape Horn twice on each voyage. The record run from Swansea to Valparaíso was sixty-eight days. Most ships could do it in seventy to seventy-five days, but some took as long as 150 days, especially if they encountered problems on the way. Rain, wind (or a lack of wind, in the Doldrums) and even ice could make progress very difficult. A cargo of coal could prove hazardous as it could and did combust and cause shipboard fires. In 1860 the *Ocean Ranger* had to put in to Tierra del Fuego because of a fire on board. Whilst waiting to extinguish the fire a group of naked islanders came on board to inspect the ship. By the time she resumed the voyage all but one of the islanders had returned to shore. The stowaway was found; the journey continued and he was taken to Swansea; he was returned home on a suitable ship at a cost of £200.

In 1875 the *Minstrel King* was hit by a whale, which passed underneath the ship, struck the rudder, and lifted the stern out of the water.

But the greatest danger was the actual rounding of Cape Horn, which has always been known to sailors as the most dangerous place on Earth, where two oceans meet and howling Antarctic gales or the westerly winds of the Southern Ocean – the 'Roaring Forties', the 'Furious Fifties' and 'Screaming Sixties' – are almost continually blowing. Such winds were a constant problem to sailing ships, especially on the east-west route, due to the funnelling effect of the Andes and the Antarctic Peninsula, which channel the winds into the relatively narrow Drake's Passage. 'Waves of up to three quarters of a mile in-between the crests and the big swells, they have three huge waves on top of them.' (Keith McKoy, sailor.) The crew up in the masts battled winds over 100 feet above deck, with the helmsman needing to be held down to the deck during hurricanes. In wet weather gear was torn to shreds by hailstones. The crews were expected to bring in two and a half acres of canvas in wild weather so that the ship didn't get 'top heavy'.

Sometimes crews had to go twenty-four hours without sleep.

Captain James Bevan was one Cape Horner who undertook the perilous voyage round the Horn fifty-six times. Captain David Morgan completed thirty-eight journeys to Chile and back during his career as a sailor and ship's captain, which meant that he made an incredible seventy-six passages round the Horn. He had to avoid icebergs on thirteen of those voyages, and on one came upon a fleet of over thirty large icebergs. On one homeward journey, Captain Morgan's ship sailed from Valparaíso, Chile, to Swansea Bay without sighting land. David Morgan had many a lucky escape, but the one that stood out in his mind was when a ferocious wave in Drake's Passage smashed the window of his ship. A piece of the shattered glass pierced through his outer oilskin coat, an overcoat, an ordinary jacket, waistcoat, jersey shirt and a vest, and inflicted a flesh wound.

On another voyage Morgan had to send a crew member up the rigging to fasten a loose topsail. It was being blown by the gale, and as it billowed out, the crewman was knocked over. He fell from the yard, hit his head on the ship's rail and was knocked unconscious and fell into the sea. There was no sign of his body, and the ship had to continue on its way as it couldn't manoeuvre a turnabout in such conditions.

Other Cape Horners included the families of captains who invited their loved ones to sail with them on the voyage, which, for the children, must have been the adventure of a lifetime, but a journey fraught with worry for the mothers.

Men and ships who made the passage safely rightly revelled in the nickname of Cape Horners, for if they arrived home safe and well they could boast that they had looked at death in one form or another. No wonder that after the homeward voyage the first pint at the Cuba public house,

Swansea, tasted so much better than the last one *before* the outward voyage at the same pub.

One who tasted such a pint was Dick Sullivan, whose story was told in the *Swansea Evening Post* in November, 1956. Dick was born at St Thomas in 1872, the son of Jim, another old Cape Horner on the San Jose. Dick stowed away on the *Tacus*, a copper barque, when he was fourteen, but he was discovered by the time the ship had reached Lundy Island and was forced to return home on the tugboat. A year later his father found him a place aboard the *Caswell*, captained by Henry Lewis. For the privilege of sending him to sea to learn his craft his parents had to pay £40. During a long life at sea Dick sailed on many ships including *Kappa*, *Foxhand*, *Thunderbolt*, *Maxima*, *Delta*, *Beta*, *L'Esperance*, *Larnacha* (a fully-rigged ship) and the *Gunford* (a four-masted ship). The names of all the Chilean ports rolled off his tongue, as did the names of some of the most important Swansea ship-owners of his period: Richardson, Henry Bath, Charles Lambert, Goldberg, Burgess, T. P. Richards, F. Tucker, Simpson Brothers and the Swansea Shipping Company. His recollections of many voyages included rough weather, gales and storms, and of being held up for a whole month at Cape Horn due to strong winds before making the passage from the South Atlantic into the Pacific. In a gale, waves would wash over the decks and the galley fire could not be lit, so the crew had to make do without hot drinks or hot meals. Sleep was almost impossible. During the same stormy month the ship lost two of her company, but there was no time to mourn lost colleagues. They had to battle on to save the ship and themselves. The cargo had to be delivered safely.

After it was unloaded, the copper ore was taken for Ticketing. Apart from Cuban copper ore, which was landed at the Cobre Wharf, all other ores were taken into storage wharves where it was weighed and registered. Before being sold, large blocks had to be broken into smaller pieces or 'bucked'. This was done by 'buckers', who were mostly Irish immigrants living in the Greenhill or Little Ireland district. Women and children would be involved in the work and each one was equipped with a heavy lump hammer and a table on which to work. Like the 'Copper Ladies' of Amlwch, they had their own uniform – an old overcoat – to protect their clothes, and each one had a pipe to smoke.

After the ore was broken into smaller pieces it was taken to a pile and labelled with a wooden label or ticket showing the quantity, vessel name, when it had arrived and when it could be sold. As soon as all the ore had been Ticketed a signal was sent from the wharf to the works' chemists to collect samples to be tested for metal content. When the results had been obtained, company representatives would tender for what they wished to buy at the Ticketing.

When the Ticketing ritual was complete the ore would be taken to the smelters. Some ore may have had to be broken into even smaller pieces before it was mixed with other ores and taken to be burnt in the calciners. What was put in the fires was carefully selected: ore that contained too much sulphur produced coarse metal, and ore that contained too little caused the metal to be lost in the slag.

Today Cape Horners and Ticketing are a very distant memory but they have added a very interesting chapter to the story of Copperopolis.

Gradually steamers superseded sailing vessels. They developed into regular traders operating under the Pacific Steam Navigation Company, the Lampert, Holt and Nautilus lines. Because they were not reliant on the wind it was not necessary for them to sail round the Horn. Instead they could take advantage of the narrower but relatively safer Magellan Straits passage. Their voyage from Chile to

Swansea could be completed in about forty-two days (compared with the sailing ships' sixty-eight to 150 days). When the Panama Canal was opened the voyage became even shorter and safer.

There was also a coastal shipping trade from Swansea. Coasters were smaller vessels of 200–250 tons that could navigate upriver on the spring tides and unload at the various wharves of the smelting works. These small steamers, schooners and barges carried, amongst other cargoes, ores from Cornwall, Anglesey and Ireland.

---

[1] *The Smelting of Copper in the Swansea District of South Wales from the Time of Queen Elizabeth to the Present Day.* Grant Francis. (Henry Sotheran & Co., 1881).
[2] *Folk Songs of Old New England.* Eloise Hubbard Linscott. (Dover Publications 1993).

Copper mining
elsewhere in Wales

14

Snowdonia's copper mines

Most geologists would consider Snowdonia primarily as a slate-mining district, with its huge quarries at Blaenau Ffestiniog, Bethesda, Llanberis and elsewhere. However, there was a lesser-known but locally important metal-mining industry, with copper-ore the chief product.

The ore occurred in a system of lodes – steeply-inclined fractures in the volcanic rocks that were filled with a mixture of minerals, some valuable and others worthless. Mineral deposition was associated with the development, some 460 million years ago during the middle of the Ordovician Period, of a large volcanic caldera forming an island in an ancient sea. Some of the eruptions were gigantic by historical standards: one is thought to have produced some 60 cubic kilometres of volcanic ash (compared to an estimated 2.79 cubic km for the catastrophic 980 Mount St Helens eruption).

It is thought that the lodes formed during the waning stages of this volcanic activity, with hot groundwaters circulating through the rocks driven by the heat from the magma-chamber. They dissolved metals from the rocks they passed through, redepositing them as ores in the lodes. The copper-iron sulphide chalcopyrite is the commonest ore mineral, but is variably accompanied by sphalerite (zinc sulphide), galena (lead sulphide), pyrite and pyrrhotite (iron sulphides) and, especially around the periphery of the mining area, arsenopyrite (iron arsenic sulphide). Traces of bismuth, tin, tungsten and gold also occur in places.

Snowdon (*Yr Wyddfa*) is Wales' highest mountain. With numerous paths to the summit, for example the PyG (*Pen y*

Gwryd) Track, and the Miners' Track (built during the 1800s for miners working the Britannia Copper Mines, abandoned in 1917), it is probably no surprise that the first refreshments sold at the summit in 1838 were served by a miner, Morris Williams.

David Bick said that 'In general, mines, like philosophies, are not newly discovered, but taken up again',[1] which may well be true of some of Snowdonia's copper mines. Not that any were mined on a large scale or made huge profits, but evidence of Roman copper smelting has been discovered in Conwy.

Writing in 1833, Samuel Lewis said of Llanberis:

Copper-ore abounds in the parish, and two copper-mines are at present worked in it: the principal of these is situated on the southern margin of the upper lake, near its highest extremity, and the other in Clogwyn Coch or the Red Rock, about half way up Snowdon, at the upper extremity of the hollow called Waun Cwm Brwynog, and near the small lake of Llyn Du yr Arddu. The former of these mines, commonly called Llyn Peris Mine, has been regularly worked for nearly a century ... the ore is sent down the lakes in boats, and conveyed by land from their lower extremity to Carnarvon, where it is shipped coast wise. The mine at Clogwyn Coch is comparatively of modern date, having been worked only a few years.[2]

Attention will be immediately be drawn to the names of some of the mines. Many have a local and even a personal ring to them, showing that such sites were well-known and used over the centuries, for example, Bron y Gadair (*bron*: breast; *cadair*: chair/seat); Pant y Wrach (*pant*: hollow; *wrach*: witch), Simdde Dylluan (*simdde*: chimney; *dylluan*: owl); Braich yr Oen (*braich*: leg; *oen*: lamb); Clogwyn

Boeth (*clogwyn*: cliff; *poeth*: hot); Moel Fleiddiau (*moel*: mound; *bleiddiau*: wolves); Pared Mawr (*pared*: wall; *mawr*: large); Derwen Deg (*derwen*: oak; *teg*: fair).

Other facts that attract attention are that so many of the owners and investors in these small mines were not local people, but from such places as Cheltenham, Cheshire, County Durham, Dublin, Leamington Spa, Lewisham, Liverpool, London, Yorkshire; and that so much money was invested in schemes that were not profit-making. They could have spent their money on much more lucrative schemes.

Companies appeared like mushrooms, being formed and set up overnight: Cwm Dyle Rock and Green Lake Copper Mining Company (1851), Great Aran and Snowdon Copper Mines (1873), Hafod y Llan Copper and Lead Mining Company, Llanberis Copper Mining Company Ltd, North Wales United Mining Company Ltd (1890). Some disappeared at the same speed!

The Snowdonia Mines are scattered through the county of Gwynedd, and it is convenient to divide the county into different regions to describe them.

1. Porthmadog and Llanfrothen

Bron y Gadair mine is situated on what used to be Richard Watkin Price's land on the Rhiwlas Estate and was believed to have been previously worked by the Romans. Price leased the land to many takers, but despite having to spend a great deal of money on the venture (for instance John Williams of Bron Eryri spent £700 on building an aqueduct in 1838), few made a profit. Probably the wisest move was that made by the Welsh Slate and Copper Mining Company (whose chairman was Lord Palmerston), which refused the venture for £1,500 in 1825 and decided to concentrate on slate quarrying. The mine's most profitable period was between

1838 and 1844. The Cambrian Mine and Quarry Company had £100,000 at their disposal in 1845, but set their sights a bit too high and failed to raise the necessary money to proceed successfully. The mine's only shaft is believed by experts to be around a hundred feet deep.

Bron y Gadair Mine was well known for being troublesome, with foul-smelling, black, sulphurous water a constant problem. A local poet, Ellis Owen of Cefn y Meysydd, wrote three *englynion*, one of which was:

> *Drws ogof, dyrus eigion, – anhoff yw*
> *A hen ffau ellyllon;*
> *Safwn tu hwnt o'r ddu-safn hon,*
> *Gorddrws Ffesiwfiws Eifion.*[3]

> [A cave entrance full of troubled waters – not a nice place;
> A den of evil spirits.
> Stand aside of this black hole
> Which is the doorstep to Eifion(ydd's) Vesuvius.]

Another problem was the local belief that the mine was haunted by a White Lady – seen by Wmffra Dafydd one Sunday night, after which he refused to work the Sunday night shift ever again!

The small mine at Pant y Wrach was situated to the east of Porthmadog. It was worked in the 1820s when lead and zinc ores were also found. By 1900 ten men worked the mine for the Pant y Wrach Copper Syndicate. During the First World War twenty-eight men found employment there, but it did not produce enough ore to be counted as a success (97 tons of copper concentrate). There are two sets of workings on two different veins, comprising opencuts (now hidden in forestry), levels, and a shaft said to be about 135 feet in depth.[4]

About a mile north-east of Pont y Wrach was the Catherine and Jane Consols, named after two unmarried sisters – Catherine and Jane Richards. This was more a lead mine than a copper mine. It was begun in 1825 and counted local Methodist preachers Richard Humphreys and Richard Jones, together with the sons of the land owner Mary Jones, Cefn Trefor, Llanfihangel y Traethau, as those who hoped to make their fortunes. By 1862 one of the shareholders condemned the mine as a 'Will o' the Wisp' and it was put up for auction at 12 noon on 2 May by T. P. Thomas at Garraway's Coffee House, Change Alley, Cornhill, London, a place described by D. Bick as 'the graveyard of scores of mining and other ventures.'[5]

It was bought and sold a number of times, the last time being 1877 when the Felix Lead Mining Company bought it. By then all the shareholders had London addresses.

Modern exploration of the site has been hampered by the many trees growing in the area.

Cae Fali is an unexplored site near the Catherine and Jane Consols.

East of the village of Rhyd are workings (mainly trial workings) marked only by building remains and deposits of waste material.

2. Cwm Pennant

In his poem *Cwm Pennant*, the poet Eifion Wyn asked:

Pam, Arglwydd, y gwnaethost Gwm Pennant mor dlws?
A bywyd hen fugail mor fyr?[6]

[Why, Lord, did you make Cwm Pennant so beautiful?
And an old shepherd's life so short?]

Though there were copper mines in the cwm, they were not

big enough to produce a scar on the landscape, as in other places seen by another poet, R. Williams Parry:

O olwg hagrwch Cynnydd
Ar wyneb trist y Gwaith.

[The ugliness of Progress
Is seen in the sad face of the Workplace.][7]

Much of the land in the cwm belonged at one time to the Brynkir Estate. The owner, Captain Joseph Huddart, on buying the estate in 1809, encouraged mining on the land, but little is known about the workings.

The Moel Hebog copper mine is situated at an altitude of 1,700 feet between the mountain of the same name and Moel yr Ogof. It was leased to William Morgan Buckingham in August 1837 with permission to work on land known as Cwm Llefrith.

Henry Marshall took over when Buckingham died and one of the conditions of the arrangement was that he had to keep four men at work for eight months of the year. The site was inaccessible due to bad weather for the other four (winter) months.

In 1853 a London advertising agent went completely overboard in his description of Dinas Great Copper in the *Mining Journal,* saying that Moel Hebog contained so much copper it would be as opening a mountainside door to get at it! Sadly he was proved wrong. The site became idle; its name was changed to Cwm Llefrith and changed again to the Glistening Valley in 1888. Forty-four men worked there, half of them underground, but it suffered as it did not have its own water supply and because of the difficulty in transporting ore from the site. In 1889 two men were injured in an explosion of blasting gelignite.

Other mines in Cwm Pennant were at Cwm Ciprwth and Gilfach. The Mining Company of Wales took over the Gilfach works in 1850 but failed its investors.

The Cwm Ciprwth Mine didn't last very long as a modern concern: only until 1889. In 1894 the mine company The Brynkir Gold Exploration Syndicate was bankrupt, throwing eighteen local men out of work.

The most notable sign of the work at Cwm Ciprwth, which survives to the present day, is the 25-foot diameter water wheel, which was made by Dingey and Son of Truro, Cornwall, whose name can be seen on the metalwork. Its large size suggests that it had to be carried in parts to Cwm Ciprwth and assembled on site. It was used to drive a water pump and a winding drum. Stone buildings still stand on the site: a smithy, a storeroom, or possibly the miners' barracks.

The Mining Company of Wales worked Blaen y Pennant (Blaen Cwm Dwyfor) in 1850, but it was taken over by the Cwm Dwyfor Copper and Silver-lead Mining Company in 1868. They boasted about possible fortunes but failed to attract investors. So few were taken in by the publicity that Thomas Harvey, managing director, had to use £500 of his own money to advertise for prospectors. By 1876, the board was in debt to the tune of £1,120 – and it was also found that Harvey had sold the company for £10,000 without letting anyone know, and that the £500 he paid for the extra advertising was from his ill-gotten gains!

The only positive note is that Blaen y Pennant was the only Snowdonia mine to have a direct link to a neighbouring port (Porthmadog) via a branch line to the Prince of Wales Slate Quarry line. Unfortunately, all its output was not enough for one train-load of ore!

3. Dyffryn Nantlle
Dyffryn Nantlle has suffered much disfigurement from the

waste of the slate quarries in the area, as told by R. Williams Parry in his poem *Y Ddôl a Aeth o'r Golwg* (The Meadow that Disappeared).[8]

It is thought that copper was mined at Drws y Coed much earlier than slate was quarried. Some believe that the Romans mined for copper there, using their method of packing quicklime into a cleft or split in the rock and leaving it there to expand until the rock split. A royal English visitor, Edward I inspected the site in 1284; in the eighteenth century lordly interest was shown by Lord Powys, whose family might have owned the land at one time.

In 1756 Richard Yarrington, the parson of nearby Llangybi, obtained a lease from William Smith, owner of the Faenol Estate, to mine for copper at Talmignedd, y Ffridd and Drws y Coed. Some miners from Cornwall were persuaded to work at nearby Simdde Dylluan but in 1777 the mine was abandoned. A problem in keeping the mine open was a lack of year-round workers. Many of the men were local farmers who were not available during harvest time. Their labours, horses and carts were needed elsewhere.

One outstanding Dyffryn Nantlle character was Marged ferch (*ferch*: daughter of) Ifan (1696–1788 or 1801). There were many sides to her character: she could compose music and play the harp and sing; she was a carpenter, a cobbler and a tailoress; she was also very strong. At over 6 feet tall, with black hair, she stood out amongst a crowd.

Marged was born at Talmignedd Ucha' farm in the copper mining region of Dyffryn Nantlle and in the early eighteenth century was landlady of a pub called Tafarn y Telyrniau at Drws y Coed. Due to her abilities and size, she could easily keep control of any rowdy customer. Playing a harp she had made herself, and singing her own compositions, she would soon calm any drunken behaviour.

Her husband was either Richard Morris or William Richards – records are confused on the matter! – who was much smaller than she was. After he had been caught drinking, she gave him such a beating that he never drank again and turned to religion.

One of the stories about her is that she had a pack of hunting terriers. The dog she liked most stole meat off a miner's table. The miner caught and killed the dog, throwing its body into the river. Marged paid him a visit and made him an offer: she suggested that if she paid four times the value of the meat, the miner could pay her the value of the dog. He foolishly refused. Marged hit him so hard that he was knocked unconscious. As he lay on the floor she went through his pockets and found enough money to pay for another dog.

When the Drws y Coed mine closed Marged ferch Ifan and her husband moved from Dyffryn Nantlle to Nant Peris and lived at Pen Llyn, near Cwm y Glo, Llanberis. There, her reputation grew even more. She had a rowing boat and was employed ferrying copper and travellers across Llyn Peris and Llyn Padarn. Her title was 'Queen of the Lakes'. When a passenger refused to pay the agreed fare, Marged threw him into the lake and charged him a guinea to be rescued! Her rowing kept her strong, so strong that she could, according to Thomas Pennant, wrestle and beat anyone.

Other stories about Marged abound. She is said to have built Pont Meibion in Nant Peris by holding up a huge piece of slate whilst workers put the other end in its proper place. Marged died shortly after the death of a favourite servant who had worked for her for over forty years. The date of Marged's death is uncertain. Some say she died in 1788. Others maintain that it was in 1801, when she would have been 105 years old. She was buried under the altar of Nant

Peris church. Poets were entranced by her legend and composed verses in her honour:

Mae gan Marged fwyn ach Ifan
Grafanc fawr a chrafanc fechan,
Un i dynnu'r cwn o'r gongl,
A'r llall i dorri esgyrn pobol.[9]

[Mild-mannered Marged, daughter of Ifan,
Has a big claw and a little claw,
One to drag the dogs from the corner
And another to break people's bones.]

More recently the land at Dyffryn Nantlle has been in the possession of the Assheton Smith family, of the Faenol Estate. In 1829, T. Assheton Smith paid £12 for a dinner for his miners, so production must have been quite high for such a celebration to have been organised. From 1804 to 1931 the mine's production was a total of 13,000 tons (roughly 500 tons per annum). Six thousand tons were taken by sea from Caernarfon harbour to Swansea between 1821 and 1840. Copper worth £1,428 was mined at Drws y Coed between 1829 and 1830 by the 114 men and four boys who worked there.

When the Assheton Smith family's interest in the mine waned (they had their slate-quarrying interest that made them a profit of about £30,000 a year (£577 a week) when the average wage for a working man was only ten shillings a week), the lease was taken over by William Forster, but until 1917 it proved to be a period of peaks and troughs. During the First World War it was re-opened, but was closed permanently in 1920, leaving a great many local men out of work.

On the southern side of Dyffryn Nantlle and to the west

of Drws y Coed copper mine can be found the remains of Talysarn Copper Mine. The owner of Simdde Dylluan (Talysarn) was also the owner of the Dorothea Slate Quarry. Richard Garanon had a controlling interest in the mine in the 1830s. From 1804 to 1931 ore production was a total of 8,000 tons. The best year's production figures were for 1832, when 1,032 tons of ore were sold to St Helens and Swansea. This was the best annual rate for any of the Snowdonia copper mines.

Many of the workforce in 1863 were Caernarfon men, as the local men preferred to labour for the higher wages of the slate quarry. The copper miners lived and slept in a small, dirty and badly-ventilated house. In 1877 work was halted, but by January 1880 it had restarted and a good supply of ore was found in December the same year. Finance was a problem by 1883 and the mine was sold in 1884. Later it was taken over by John Thomas, a Caernarfon auctioneer, who raised enough capital in 1907 to be able to employ twelve men to work underground, a figure which had increased to thirty-five by 1909. In 1914, the works closed. It was the deepest mine in Snowdonia, with shafts of a depth of 116 fathoms (696 feet).

During its working days Benallt, a small, nearby mine, was owned by a number of different companies: the Pen'allt Silver-lead Mining Company; the Great Mountain Silver-lead Mining Company; the Mining Corporation of Great Britain (1878); the Benallt Copper & Lead Mines Ltd (1906); the Consolidated Zinc & Lead Mines Ltd (1917); the Nantlle Vale Mineral Leases Ltd (1925). During its life it suffered a great deal from over-optimistic owners, over-ripe publicity and fraud by some of the directors, who had to face legal proceedings. Although never successful, the mine struggled on until 1931.

Gwernore copper mine dates from as early as 1755. In

1843, six men bargained for £2 per ton of ore, but had 10 shillings per month deducted to pay for the use of an engine to turn the water wheel.

Ffridd Isaf mine was situated near Rhyd-ddu but was not worked after 1863, and the labours of John Griffith, Porthmadog, and James Hamer of Reddish Green, Stockport, were all in vain.

4. Beddgelert

Brynfelin copper mine was opened sometime before 1760 and had its most productive period during the eighteenth century. The nineteenth century proved to be one of repeated failures for the mine, despite some flashes of hope such as in 1838, when the Brynyfelin Company, manager Robert Byres, wished to buy the Sugyn copper mine, Beddgelert, Gwynedd, but failed. At that time twenty girls were employed as copper dressers in the mine. Their wages were poor, but they proved to be an invaluable asset to the mine and its owners. Mr Byres had plans for a road, an office, and a drying room for the girls' clothes, but hard times forced him to consider selling the venture in 1842; yearly returns show that only a little ore was sold at Swansea: 685 tons in 1840–41, none in 1843 and only 41 tons in 1844. In 1851, the mine faced insurmountable difficulties due to a lack of ore and had closed by 1861.

Advertisements appeared in the *Carnarvon & Denbigh Herald* in 1864 offering the property for sale, but ten years later it was dying a slow death, never to be resurrected.

At the Lefel Goch mine, an adit had been driven into the ground that was so long that there was no air or ventilation. This rendered it unworkable.

Plenty of copper was found at Aberglaslyn, but as it was mixed with other ores it was very difficult to separate, resulting in a low annual output – only 56 tons in 1838/39.

Cwm Bychan (Nantmor) mine was opened in 1720 and had its heyday between 1782 and 1802. Nantmor miners were such renowned tunnelers that they were asked to dig and drive tunnels at the Oakley Slate Quarries, some of which were named after the workers.

A mile long ropeway, supplied by R. White & Sons of Widnes, was built but carried very little ore from the mine to the crushing mill. After a working life of over 200 years, the mine went into voluntary liquidation in 1925.

Financial problems bedevilled Cribddu and Sygun mines from their start at about 1800 due to the fact that they mined poor quality ore, and very little of it. From 1804 to 1931 only 1,500 tons of ore was brought to the surface. There were also many 'comings and goings' amongst the personnel, and those that were in charge, whether they were owners or agents, built their investors' hopes up with what proved to be false promises.

5. Nant Gwynant

Braich yr Oen and Hafod y Llan were two copper mines that were worked in conjunction with one another. They were leased by Margaret Lynne of Bodysgallen to Hugh Davies for twenty-one years from 22 July 1762. On 29 September 1794 they were leased by Lord Mostyn to Robert Hodgson of Congleton, Edward Hawkins of Macclesfield, and Abraham Mills of Hurdsfield.

In April 1862 copper was scarce in both mines and the miners were instructed to look for gold- bearing quartz. They didn't have much luck, and by 1883 only five men worked underground at the mine. To add to their troubles the February storms of 1884 washed away parts of the works, including the blacksmith's smithy and the dressing floor. Within another two years the mine closed for good.

Hafod y Porth mine dates from 1755. An 1873 plan of

the mine shows nine lodes of copper, 'the majority of which amounted to little more than a gleam in the promoter's eyes'.7

Lliwedd copper mine is situated in Cwm Erch. After a slow start at the end of the seventeenth century, the author of a sales promotion leaflet was hopeful that up to 200 men could be employed there, but from 1804 to 1931 only 2,000 tons of ore was raised (15.75 tons per annum), which was not a very good return from the labours of 200 men – if that many were ever employed!

6. Snowdon

The Snowdon (or Britannia) supply of copper ore is at 2,000 feet, located above Llyn Glaslyn, and was discovered during the last decade of the eighteenth century. Barracks for the miners were built, but in winter weather they had to endure real hardship before they could even begin to work. In 1801 a tunnel had to be cut through 20 yards of deep snow before the mine could be reached. By 1804/05 a 4-mile path had been made from the summit to the shores of Llyn Cwellyn to bring the copper ore down on sledges. It had to be carried on men's backs from the far side of the summit, and then a team of two horses, worked by a seventy-year old man, dragged the 6 hundredweight load down the path on the sledge. It was then carted to Caernarfon. A new road from Llanberis to Pen-y-gwryd was a much needed improvement.

Between 1804 and 1842 the ore was sent to Swansea, but the cost of transportation for the first part of its journey to Caernarfon proved to be prohibitive. Injections of cash were sought in 1847 and again in 1850. Shares were sold to finance the Snowdon copper mines. The twenty-four men who worked there needed the support more than anyone.

In September 1851 the Cwm Dyle Rock and Green Lake

Copper Mining Company led another revival. One of their cost-saving methods was to use local peat as fuel for their smelting furnaces. The workforce at that time was quite cosmopolitan, with miners from Wales, England, France and Belgium. In May 1852 the company advertised for a French-speaking mine captain. They appointed an English-speaking Cornishman, Thomas Colliver.

Conditions at the works were slow to improve and by 1854 a debt of £16,059 was shown on the balance sheet. Life and work for the miners was very difficult. On one occasion, in April 1854, a boat carrying a load of ore sank twice during one journey on one of Snowdonia's lakes. Bad weather hampered work during the harsh winter months.

The mine was sold in 1857 to the Cwm Dyle Copper Mining Company, which had £2,000 in the bank and offices at the British Hotel, Bangor. Richard Williams Bulkeley of Baron Hill, Beaumaris, pitched in with £200 of his own money and a further £250 from elsewhere. In September 1861 the company was able to pay its shareholders a dividend for the first time in a number of years. Good times seemed close at hand, but in reality they never arrived and the works were put up for sale in April 1863. No one came forward to make an offer. Eventually it was put up for auction at the British Hotel, Bangor, on 18 January 1865.

On 25 May 1871 another purchaser bought the works at a sale held at the Pen-y-gwryd Hotel. Edmund Spargo stepped forward, together with Sir Richard Williams Bulkeley and others. Spargo himself was appointed works manager. He organised the re-laying of a tram road, built new barracks for the miners, laid down a new dressing room floor for new machinery, surfaced a new cart road and built a 9-foot high, 40-foot long new dam at Glaslyn. Unfortunately for him and all others concerned, very little copper ore was found, and in April 1875 the mine closed.

It wasn't until 1888 that the next chapter in the history of the mine began, when Edward Herzberg Harmount of 58 Lombard Street, London, became the holder of the lease. He spent £38,000 in eight years before going bankrupt. After him, the North Wales United Mines Company Limited tried. They employed forty-two miners and thirty-five surface workers. They failed. The Britannia Copper Mine Ltd also tried. This company was formed in 1898. It built a new manager's house on the shores of Llyn Llydaw. They found 1,208 tons of ore in the first two years of operation, but the price of copper fell dramatically and the works stopped in 1904.

Other companies who worked the mine were the Snowdon and Dalawin Copper Mines (1847); Great Snowden Copper Mining Company (1873), and the Britannia Copper Mine Ltd (1898).

On a more accessible site, close to Llyn Du'r Arddu, is Clogwyn Coch mine, but work could not be guaranteed all year round due to harsh winters. It is thought (but it has never been confirmed) that Snowdon Mine and Clogwyn Coch had an underground connection. True or not, it helped neither of them. The Llanberis mines, divided into different units (Lower Works, Yew Tree Works, Smithy Works, Bridge Works) were situated near the head of Llyn Peris and were part of the Faenol Estate. Boats were used to carry ore along the lake. Despite having four different units it was not a huge complex and was only 300 yards from end to end.

Spiritual assistance was received from the Reverend Archdeacon Ellis of Bangor, who with his sons Hugh and William, and William Bridge, were running the mines. Hugh and William were also involved with the Dinorwig Slate Quarry and were possibly more experienced and more involved than the Archdeacon. Arthur Aitkin, on a very short visit to Llanberis, described the works:

> The mine consists of several horizontal galleries driven
> into Snowdon; the rock is hard with an hornblende
> schitzus, the matrix quartz; the metal is a rich yellow ore,
> containing copper in unison with sulphur, the quality
> procured is not very considerable.[10]

Arthur Aitkin could see this, while others, who ploughed
their money into the venture, appeared to be blind to its
failings.

Charles Roe & Co., Macclesfield; Thomas Wright,
Nantwich (1805); William & Thomas Jones, Wrexham
(1821); Richard Griffith & Partners (1836), were others
who had more money than sense and invested heavily in the
mines. By 1841 no ore was being sold and so it continued
until 1850, but between 1870 and 1875 seventy-five tons of
ore, containing 34 per cent copper (perhaps the highest
copper content of any copper ore found in Britain) were dug
up to the surface. So hopeful was Wallace Cragg, a director
of Glynrhonwy Slate Quarry, that in 1873 he signed a forty-
year lease on behalf of the Llanberis Copper Mining
Company Ltd, but by 1876 his company was in dire straits
and by 1885 it was dissolved.

Today the remains of the mines are partially concealed
under Llyn Peris, and the lake now is the lower reservoir of
the Dinorwig Power Station.

7. Nant Ffrancon
Copper ore was discovered at the Gwaith site, below Cwm
Graianog, in 1782. The exploration of the site and
subsequent discovery was supervised by William Williams
of Llandygai.

Cwm Ceunant mine had three levels which were 60 feet

apart. Copper ore was first discovered at Ceunant sometime after 1760 when explorations were made by Archdeacon Ellis, Mr Hughes of Penrhyn and others. More arsenic than copper was raised here and in 1837 the river was so polluted that it affected the men's health, and the works closed.

Three men – Sir George Young, Ellis Hughes and Francis Lloyd (an Anglesey doctor) – were willing, in 1760, to put money into a venture to open a mine at Dolawen but found that they could not work together. Mr Climo, a Cornishman, then ran the mine for Roe & Co.

In 1822 another trio – Evan Griffith, Thomas Meyrick, Robert Griffith, all Anglesey men – took a twenty-one year lease on Dolawen and Ceunant with a promise to keep four experienced miners at work for nine months of the year. They had some success and sold 128 tons of ore at Swansea between 1836 and 1839. In April of 1836 they sold eight tons for the very high price of £15 12s. 6d. per ton. By 1847 shares were being offered to the public under a new lease by Captain Pennant. Today the remains are under waste materials from the Penrhyn Slate Quarry.

It was said that the miners worked at Coed y Ddinas round the clock for ten years from 1760 to 1770, but they had no real success.

8. Conwy

The Derwen Deg mine was opened in 1860. Twenty years later it had reached a depth of 18 fathoms (108 feet).

In March 1878 the Derwen Deg and Panol Gwyn Copper and Lead Mining Company took over but its name was almost longer than its tenure at the mine. It was bought for £100,000 by the North Wales Freehold Copper Mining and Smelting Company. In October of that year, they had arranged a special deal with the London and North Western Railway Company to carry ore to Vivian's of Swansea. By

June 1882 the mining company was in liquidation due to serious flooding at the mine.

The Bwlch mine near Deganwy has very little written history but was shown on a map of 1837. It is one of only two places in Britain where antimony has been mined.

9. Ffestiniog

In an area which has a reputation as a slate-quarrying area, small copper workings or trials are known of, such as Moel Fleiddiau, three miles north-west of Blaenau Ffestiniog near the source of the river Lledr.

In 1850 shares were sold in the Newborough (Offeren) venture. The money was well-spent and gold was (allegedly) found. The British Silver-Lead Mining Company Ltd bought the works in July 1878 from David Roberts, who held the land, from Lord Newborough, hence the name, but metal prices were very low at the time which resulted in the venture failing.

A trial on the banks of the river Gamallt was abandoned in 1880. At nearby Llynau Gamallt, another trial was held in 1892 but worked by only two or three men at the most.

In 1888 the Cwm Cynfal site was owned by John Roberts & Partners of Sunderland, who ran the Cynfal Mining Company, which employed up to ten men who worked underground.

1 *The Old Copper Mines of Snowdonia.* David Bick. Pound House, 1982).
2 *Wales – a Topographical Dictionary.* Samuel Lewis, 1833.
3 Old newspaper cutting given to author by W. Owen, Borth y Gest.
4 *Old Copper Mines of Snowdonia.* Bick.
5 *Telynegion Maes a Môr.* E. Williams. (Caernarfon, 1906).
6 *Cerddi'r Gaeaf.* R. Williams Parry. (Gwasg Gee, 1964).
7 *The Old Copper Mines of Snowdonia.* David Bick. Pound House, 1982).
8 *Cerddi'r Gaeaf. Op. cit.*
9 *Merched Gwyllt Cymru.* Beryl H. Griffiths. (Gwasg Gwynedd, April 1007).
10 *Journal of a Tour through North Wales.* Arthur Aitkin. (London, 1797).

15

Flintshire's copper factories

The town and industries of Holywell have benefited from the waters that feed the holy well of Saint Winefride since the eighth century. Lead and other ores were found in the limestone rocks of the area. Attempts to mine the ores were made in the late sixteenth and early seventeenth centuries.

Other works and their owners found fewer problems and success came easier to them. A red-lead mill, an iron forge and three wire mills were built around 1728 near Basingwerk Abbey Farm, in Greenfield Valley, near Holywell, Flintshire. These needed constant water to supply power for a tilting hammer. They also needed plenty of storage space to rest iron ingots for up to eight weeks after they had been hammered and annealed. After soaking, they were further worked on in the forge and wire mills.

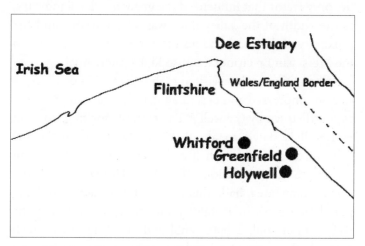

Sketch map showing some important industrial sites in Flintshire

One of the original owners, Benjamin Perrin, sold out to a Mr Smedley, who rebuilt most of the Greenfield Works. Unfortunately he did not have a good head for business and was made bankrupt in 1779. The site was then purchased by the Parys Mine Company (see earlier chapters).

By the early nineteenth century new techniques were used and the amount of pollution was not so objectionable. Holywell became a growing town with a population of over 5,500 by 1800, many of whom were attracted by the employment offered by corn mills, paper mills and cotton mills, copper rolling and wire mills, and a brass-making works.

The Holywell stream provided hydro-power, first used by the monks of Basingwerk Abbey for grinding corn. Later, technological advances during the Industrial Revolution saw more sophisticated machinery being used to harness the energy produced by the stream. Water from the well flowed at a constant 4,000 gallons per minute. It also had the advantage of never freezing as it was always at a temperature of 47 degrees Celsius. The presence of the stream was not the only factor that influenced the growth of local industry, as the width of the valley floor was advantageous and the proximity of the coast and port facilities on the Dee and on the Mersey in Liverpool was also highly influential.

When Daniel Defoe visited Holywell in 1724 or 1725, he was not impressed and described it, rather contemptuously, as 'a little town by the well'.[1] The earliest smelting works at Holywell is dated to about 1733. By the time Samuel Johnson visited almost half a century later, the town had grown to a population of 2,000. Holywell and the surrounding area had, then, one of the fastest-growing population rates in Britain. Johnson reported seeing the well, a flour mill, a paper mill and 'a tilting mill', which worked off a water wheel and in which iron was worked and split 'as quick as by the hand'.[2] Lower down the valley he saw a wire mill and such was his delight and enjoyment that he gave the workers the grand sum of one shilling!

According to Thomas Pennant, the first Holywell copper works was owned by Thomas Patten of Warrington, a merchant steeped in his family's tradition in the sugar, tea and tobacco trade. He entered the business world in 1717 by establishing the family copper smelting works. The Warrington Company, which he founded in 1756, moved to Greenfield, near Holywell, as the availability of local coal and an easily navigable river facilitated his work. He already owned a copper works at Bank Quay, Warrington. In the early 1740s he took over the forge, the charcoal works and the pool, and by 1743 had added more land to his enterprise. In 1752 he transferred his holdings to another company he was involved with, the Cheadle Brass Company, which built two other works close by. The Warrington Company was established in 1755: copper was plated, rolled and formed, 'into vessels of any kind or size to be exported.'[3]

At the Battery Mill many of the workers were local people, who lived in the thirty-five purpose-built terraced cottages of Battery Row. They were employed in shaping pots and pans from brass sheets. Built by the Greenfield Copper and Brass Company, such houses were of a high standard compared to others at the time, and comprised two downstairs rooms and two upstairs bedrooms, with a spacious landing. There were even cellars in the largest houses. Holywell Urban District Council saw fit to demolish the whole terrace in the 1960s. By 1765 the Warrington Company had acquired more land and had constructed a pond by Battery Row. Patten also built a brass-ware plant to make bowls, pans and rods. In 1766 the Warrington Company built a Battery Mill for copper and brass in Holywell.

In a battery factory or mill (here, 'battery' means beating or hammering) the work was done by using water-powered hammers up to 500 lbs in weight. A brass ingot of 70 lbs would be hammered into a plate or sheet to be cut into circular shapes. Four or five of the shapes would then be hammered together. These plates of brass would be shaped by hand into bowls on an anvil. A later development in the battery mill was the use of rollers to flatten ingots into sheets and the finished product was used for coin-making.

To produce a ton of copper from ten tons of ore required thirty tons of coal. The copper produced by Patten's companies helped build up a large family fortune by supplying slave trade copper in Liverpool: copper vessels and trinkets used as currency with the slave-traders on African coasts.

The water-wheel connected to the mill's machines was powered by water from Battery Pond. This was the site visited by Dr Johnson, where he saw the use made of the stream 'by the great copper companies, those behemoth of commerce, our little Jordan was soon drunk up.'[4]

Ore mined by the Parys Mine Company on Anglesey had been smelted in Ravenhead near St Helen's, at Swansea, and also at the Temple Mills in Buckinghamshire. Thomas Williams made sure the Greenfield works were expanded to cope with the work. Ingots were made into Neptunes (a type of dish) or saltpans and other items to be used in the slave trade.

Surprising as it may seem, the Welsh copper industry and the trans-Atlantic slave trade were connected. As mentioned earlier, Thomas Williams claimed to have invested £70,000 in the slave trade. In July 1788 he petitioned the House of Commons, on behalf of himself and his co-partners in the manufacture of brass battery, and other copper, brass and mixed metal goods, for the African trade at Holywell in the county of Flint, Penclawdd, in the county of Glamorgan, and Temple Mill in the county of Berks.

Although Williams' ships probably never carried slaves, his produce certainly played its part in the 'triangular trade', in which British ships sailed to the west coast of Africa with their cargoes of copper and brass trinkets and cheap jewellery to exchange for human beings. They, in turn, were carried across the Atlantic to be sold as slaves. The ships made the return journey to Britain with cargoes of coffee, cotton, rice, sugar and tobacco.

Williams' development of copper bolts for ship's timbers led to much of his success and he secured a monopoly in their production after securing a patent. A new company, the Greenfield Copper and Brass Company, was formed to take over the production of the bolts. A new copper rolling mill was built in Greenfield in 1787 and yet another, the Meadow Mill, in 1788, which specialized in producing copper rollers for printing on different materials – muslin in particular. Holywell was the site chosen to make the copper sheets for sheathing ships' bottoms for the Merchant Navy and Royal Navy. Cake copper from Ravenhead was rolled between cast iron rollers 18 inches in diameter and 4 ft 6 inches long into sheets and bolts. The navy contract asked for 25,000 bolts a week, but the mill actually produced 40,000. Nearby was a wire mill, possibly the Abbey Wire Mill, making copper wire, nails and tacks. Wire drawing from a sheet of copper was a manual process where the men, sitting opposite each other in swings, would attach a thin sheet to a girdle fastened around their waists. The swings were pushed away from each other and the brass pulled until it was flexible enough to be stretched into wire.

The main mill building was 86 feet long by 69 feet wide, with a copper roof supported by two pillars 11½ feet apart.

Three cast iron waterwheels powered the machinery – they were 20 feet in diameter, and turned by water from a pool with a surface area of 117,028 square feet. Copper ingots were melted down and moulded into plates 3 feet by 4 feet, ½ inch thick, before being cut into strips which were then passed through rollers to make larger but thinner sheets. Later some of the plates would be sent to the wire mills and others cut into circular shapes to be sent to the battery mill.

The smaller Meadow Mill housed the rollers to make copper rollers for printing on muslin cloth.

Much of the mill's produce was sent to Trelawnyd to be made into nails and pins. What was left was sent to nail-making companies in St Helens.

Williams and one of his partners, John Wilkinson of Bersham, were responsible for replacing the old wooden water wheels with new cast iron ones. Together with his salesman, Pascoe Grenfell, Williams helped Holywell works to gain fame as far as North America and throughout Europe. Many visitors from both continents came visiting, including Augustin Lentin, mentioned earlier.

Holywell companies tasted much success. By 1780 the Parys Mine Company had taken over much of the site. Copper ore from Parys Mountain was sent by the Warrington Company to the Stanley Works at St. Helens to be smelted. The copper ingots formed there were sent on to Greenfield to be turned into various articles to be sold.

By 1780 the copper works of the valley were the property of the Parys Mine Company from Anglesey, on land leased from Sir Pyers Mostyn:

> Thomas Williams, esquire, that useful and active character, with unparalleled speed covered the lower part of the stream, or that next to the sea, with buildings stupendous in extent and ingenuity of contrivance.

These great works are under the firm of the Parys Mine Company. The buildings were completed in the year 1780.[5]

What attracted the company and others to the area was a plentiful supply of coal and the ever-flowing Holywell Stream, together with the facilitating Dee, which meant that ships could land their cargo of ores in Greenfield and send out their merchandise to other parts of the demanding world. Greenfield is now an industrial heritage park.

By 1790 Thomas Williams had considerable influence on the copper market. He was also, by then, the owner of the Cheadle Brass Company in Holywell, and had formed other companies which had works in Stanley, Liverpool and Swansea. His assets amounted to at least a million pounds (worth £56,030,000 in 2011). Over a thousand tons of coal a day were consumed in his works at Holywell and Liverpool. At the same time, he had between thirty and forty ships constantly employed in carrying ore to Holywell or taking his produce to different markets. A number of works at Holywell were engaged in making brass pans for the sugar industry of the West Indies, copper cauldrons for the tea merchants of Ceylon and India, and a vast amount of trinkets for the African market. He also had contracts from the Admiralty in London for providing copper sheets and bolts for sheathing ship's bottoms, as well as from the Dutch, French and Spanish governments.

Thomas Williams was one of a group of industrialists who had plans for a canal from Holywell to the Dee to improve port facilities for their ships. The plans went before Parliament in 1788; work started, but was never completed because war with France broke out in 1793.

In 1798 the Reverend Richard Warner visited and was pleasantly surprised by what he saw. He was on holiday in

Wales, walking twenty-six miles a day and recording his travels in letters which he published: *A Walk through Wales* in 1799, followed by *A Second Walk through Wales* in 1800. In his letters from Holywell, he mentions that he had seen four cotton factories, five copper and brass mills belonging to the Mona Mines Company, and others belonging to the Greenfield Brass and Copper Company. He reckoned that about 600 people were employed in the copper and brass mills and that the population of Holywell was over 5,000. His writings provide an eye-witness account of what took place in the mills:

> The calamine used in its (brass) composition is brought from the great mines ... being first roasted in order to divest it of sulphur, with which, in the raw state, it is combined. It is then cleansed and separated from the lead also, which always accompanies it, and undergoes the process of calcinations. A pounding mill next receives it, where a quantity of ground charcoal is mixed, and pounded with it.'[6]

He continues with a full description of how copper and zinc were mixed to make brass and made into various different utensils:

> These works are chiefly employed at present in making articles for the African Company, such as broad shallow pans for the procuring of salt from saltwater by evaporation, and manilas, small baubles, somewhat resembling a horseshoe in shape, between two and three inches in diameter, disposed of to the Africans, and by them used as current coin, being strung on a copper wire and worn round their waists.[7]

Other articles made for the home market included large pans and smaller utensils, which were shaped out of flat sheets and:

> cut to that shape by steel scissors worked by water and a proper thickness, by being subjected to the action of heavy hammers worked by the same power, which beat upon them with such astonishing velocity as to give from one to eight hundred strokes in a minute. The utensil is held the while by a workman who sits at the side of the battering hammer, and continues moving it under the blows of the engine, till it has assumed the form required. A small peg then stops the motion of the waterwheel, the hammer loses its power in a moment, the intonations cease, and all is quiet and silent.[8]

He also visited the Wire Mill, where rods of copper were:

> drawn into strings of any given thickness, by the action of an engine, that pulls them through holes bored in iron plates, [this] concluded a survey of the most interesting, amusing, and instructive nature. The numbers of manufacturers employed in these works are about six hundred.[9]

Another visitor was Thomas Pennant (1726–1798), whose works about the history of Holywell and Whitford include many details and facts of the history of the copper industry in the Greenfield Valley. His first work was first about experimental smelting of different ores in a furnace that he had built himself at Downing, near Holywell. On his *Tours of Wales*, his travelling companion was the artist Moses Griffith.

Thomas Williams' death on 19 November 1802 signalled the end of an exciting period for Holywell and the Flint Copper Industry. His son Owen inherited his father's businesses, but not his business acumen. Together with Pascoe Grenfell, he formed a new company named Williams and Grenfell. In 1806 a new Copper Wire Mill was built to specialise in the production of copper nails and spikes for the government, but business suffered due to a number of factors: higher-quality Chilean ore was being imported to Swansea, and Anglesey supplies were dwindling; the Dee began to silt up and even small ships of 40 to 50 tons had difficulty in navigating it; flooding in the Flintshire coalmines was a regular occurrence; steam engines had been developed to produce power; Muntz metal, a cheaper and more efficient alternative to copper, was used to sheath ships from 1832 onwards; wars with North America and France had an adverse effect on the industry, and there was a change in technique from battering copper and brass to using casting methods.

Gradually, all the Williams & Grenfell assets came under Grenfell's control and were moved to Swansea, which had its own local supply of coal and much better port facilities to deal with incoming ships from abroad carrying ore. By about 1840 Anglesey and Holywell's best days in the copper industry were far behind them.

The effect of dirt, fumes and noise on the population was significant. In Holywell one of the Mostyn family mansions was turned into an office for the Parys Mine Company, and Thomas Pennant was forced to leave and partly demolish his home at Bagillt Hall. What became of the ordinary workers and their homes is not known. More than likely they had to stay and suffer.

[1] *The Greenfield Valley.* K. Davies and C. J. Williams. (Holywell Town Council, 1986).
[2] *Ibid.*
[3] *Ibid.*
[4] *Ibid.*
[5] *Ibid.*
[6] *Ibid.*
[7] *Ibid.*
[8] *Ibid.*
[9] *Ibid.*

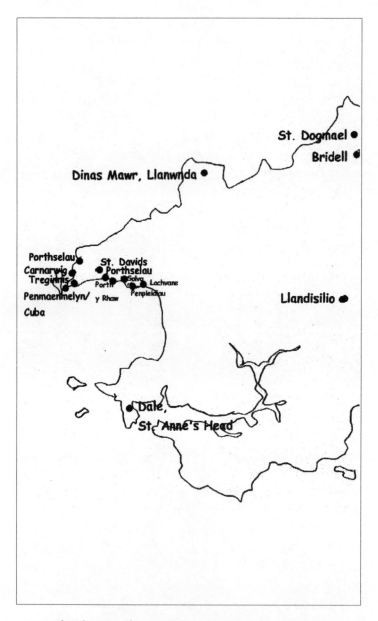

Sketch map of some important copper mining sites in Pembrokeshire

16

Copper mines in Pembrokeshire

The county of Pembrokeshire, in the most westerly part of Wales, was at one time a copper-mining centre, though most of the mines and workings were small and worked by only a few men compared to the other hives of industry in such places as Holywell, Parys Mountain or Swansea. The remains of these copper mines are to be found mainly to the north of St Brides Bay, and many were close to the coast. This resulted in much waste being thrown into the sea, and what ore was found was shipped from the small harbours of Solva and Porthclais to be smelted at Burry Port or Swansea. Never the busiest of industries in the county, it was 'confined to a scattering of small producers and trials'.[1]

Possibly the most publicity the Pembrokeshire copper-mining industry received was early in May 1883, when John Reynolds died as a result of an accident at the Treginnis Mine, near St David's. He was in a bucket being raised to the surface which fell about 15–20 feet back to the bottom of the shaft. Though not named as the one who worked the bucket and lifting gear, John Rees was working at the bottom of the tunnel. Other workers known to have been present were John Nicholas, John Price and Henry Tregan. Reynolds became paralysed due to a broken neck. From his sick bed he wrote a statement claiming that his fellow workers had been 'larking at his expense'[2] and had let the rope fall freely. They, on the other hand, blamed the poor state of the machinery they had to work with.

John Reynolds died on 4 May 1883. An inquest was held at which HM Inspector of Mines described the machinery as being quite old but not necessarily dangerous. He did, however, suggest modernisations and modifications which could have made the mine safer. The jury found that Reynolds had died as a result of injuries sustained after falling out of the bucket. The other miners were strongly condemned for their foolish actions.

Both winchmen appeared in the Mathry Sessions on 8 June, and were acquitted of a charge of manslaughter. George Owen Williams, the owner, closed the mine, thus bringing to an end copper mining in extreme west Wales.

Copper mining had begun on Treginnis Isaf farm land (near St David's) in the 1820s. In 1827, Henry Harries (the then occupier), and James and John Stephens (two Edinburgh brothers) started the search for copper at the old site of Penmaenmelyn Mine. Shafts were sunk; adits were built to drain away water but profits for the owners and workers were small. The mine closed in 1836. James Stephens died in 1837 while in Scotland. His widow, Margaret Davies of St David's, was left his estate, but with a young family to nurse, and no help from her brother-in-law, who returned to Scotland, her connection with the mine was severed.

On the death of Henry Harries in 1851, Treginnis farm and the mine became the property of Samuel Williams, Y Fagwr, St David's. Williams was a busy merchant and ship-owner who sold the property to 'Squire' Llewellyn in 1856. He showed very little interest in the property and no further developments took place until it was purchased by George Owen Williams (eldest son of Samuel Williams, a previous owner), and re-opened in 1871, when Being an enthusiastic amateur scientist, Williams commissioned a survey to report on prospects. The report refers to ore with a copper content of almost 10 per cent. These results were favourable enough for him to consider selling his property for £10,000. Unfortunately, there were no takers, so he had to use his own money to develop the mine and another smaller venture at Porth Taflod. Conditions at both sites were very primitive: they had a hand-operated winch, with a rope over a pulley on a wooden tripod placed over the shaft head, used to raise about one hundredweight of ore and a miner at the same time.

Hopes were high in the late 1870s when there was talk of building a local railway to facilitate the moving of ore, but the railway was never built, despite Thomas Evans, a mine agent and engineer, writing in the *Mining Journal* of January 1877, describing the local copper of Treginnis as being of the best quality, 'both for the percentage of metal contained and for the facility for smelting'.[3]

In 1885 the site was sold to J. B. Evans, of Dowlais. In the sale description, ore with a copper content of 17 per cent is quoted. Evans later came to an agreement with a consortium of south Wales businessmen, including Albert Charles Macintosh (gentleman) of Penarth, Edward Howell (vestry clerk), John Guthrie (ship owner), James Radley (merchant) and Arthur Llewelyn Hopkins (merchant), all of Cardiff, to search for copper and sink shafts. They were joined by the local mine agent Thomas Evans, ever hopeful of finding a fortune. The owner was to be paid 4d. per £1 on any ore found and sold. Nothing came of the grand plans and the agreement was dissolved.

Thomas Evans' motto must have been, 'If at first you don't succeed; try, try again', for another letter from his pen appeared in the *Mining Journal* in 1891: 'A respectable syndicate has been formed lately to explore several lodes of copper, &c, near the city of St David's, and the experts have good confidence in the mine, and believe that it is a good plot of mineral only requiring proper opening up'.[4] He also mentioned a copper lode containing 26 per cent copper. By then, the bottom had fallen out of the small mines copper industry and his appeal for new syndicate members went unanswered.

George Owen Williams made one other attempt in 1897 to make his fortune. Again he offered his property at Treginnis for sale – this time for only £6,000! He even offered it for rent but still no takers were found.

On some tithe maps of the area, Treginnis is named as 'Cuba'. An area of Swansea had the same name during the heyday of its copper industry. Doubtless there is a connection.

Along the 186 miles of the Pembrokeshire Coast Path are most of the county's sites where copper was sought but never found in sufficient quantities. On starting from the northern end of the path, the first site to be encountered would be St Dogmaels, where copper ore was discovered in 1851. Nearby is Tŷ Gwyn (*tŷ*: house; *gwyn*: white) in Bridell, where there was a working copper and gold mine in 1865. Further along is Newport, which had a small copper mine but all signs have by now disappeared and the exact location is not known. At Dinas Mawr, Llanwnda, on the north side of Pwll Deri, an adit was built into the cliff at Aber Twm.

Close to St David's, on the west side of Porthselau, can be found Ogof Felen (*ogof*: cave, *melyn*: yellow), another site which has been mined in the past, but like most Pembrokeshire ventures had very little to show for all the effort put in. Carnarwig is one of the oldest sites of a disused copper mine in Pembrokeshire, dating from around 1585.

Some sites have retained their old Welsh names such as Penmaenmelyn (*pen*: headland, *maen*: stone, *melyn*: yellow). Porth Taflod (*porth*: bay/harbour, *taflod*: loft) is another such name and was used as a name for a Treginnis Mine shaft. Carnochor is situated 'Eastward of St David's, about a mile, by the sea side ... they find a sort of Oar in the veins of the Rock which glitters like Copper.'[5] (This is from the Thomas Tomkins manuscript, kept in the Bodleian Library in Oxford: Tomkins (1572–1656) was a St David's-born composer of the late Tudor period.) This is possibly the earliest copper mining site in Pembrokeshire, dating from the reign of the Tudors. Another such site is at Penpleidiau.

A very descriptive Welsh name is Porth y Rhaw (*porth*: bay/harbour; *rhaw*: spade) to the west of Llanunwas. Llanunwas is to the west of Solva. It is possible that copper was found on the slopes but as it was a difficult site to reach it could well have been too treacherous to work. Ogof Mwn (*ogof*: cave, *mwyn*: minerals/ores) is 600 yards west of Porth y Rhaw. Steps named Smugglers' Steps lead down to the cave. This is another of a number of local names which suggest the presence of copper ore or mining. Carnuwchwrn mine was on land owned by the Bishopric of St David's but leased to Canon Holcombe. A man-made tunnel through the cliff shows some sign of mining, but it has not been worked since at least 1833.

Ben James (owner) leased land at Dinas Fawr, Lochvane to Edward Watkin Scale, 'a gentleman of St David's'[6], for twenty-one years in 1847, hoping for payment of 12 shillings per ton of copper. The work was closed in 1890.

A parish with the very modern-sounding name of St. Elvis, actually named in memory of St Ailbe, had a small silver/lead/copper mine at Dinas Fawr. Hugh Wynne of Llanboidy wrote to the Bishop of St David's in 1769 with information about a find of copper ore on his land at Dale on St Anne's Head, on the northern edge of Frenchman's Bay, which was very close to the bishopric's land as well. Wynne was of a mind to work there by himself, but the venture was very short-lived; by the time of an 1833 report all signs of its presence had disappeared.

Land belonging to John Francis Meyrick of Bush at South Hook, Herbrandston, was leased from John Gilby in 1785 by Sir Richard Philipps, Lord Milford, who had high hopes of discovering copper.[7]

The most easterly sites on the journey would take the traveller to Martletwy where a lease for lead and copper mining was granted in 1798, but only coal was raised on the site. In Llandisilio, on land west of Rhydwen farm, a copper mine was worked before 1849 but, like some of the others, yielded very little.

Many, if not most, of the above sites were small and very difficult to work. Few machines were used, as the mines were difficult to reach, and therefore the rock had to be broken by hand. The rubble that was removed could, in most cases, be thrown over the cliffs into the sea. Today, little evidence survives of how and where men worked so hard.

[1] *A List of Mines in Pembrokeshire and the adjoining parts of Carmarthen and Ceredigion.* Peter Claughton, Dept of History, Exeter University, April 1999).

[2] *Forgotten Mines.* P. B. S. Davies. (Merrivale Publications, 1990).

[3] *Ibid.*

[4] *Ibid.*

[5] *Ibid.*

[6] *Ibid.*

[7] Mason and Bevins, *British Mining,* 71 (2002), 5–12.

17

Other small copper-mining ventures in Wales

If potential investors suspect there is copper underground, they have to 'speculate before they can accumulate'. It costs money to dig a trial shaft or adit, to try to find a lode or vein. At that point, not knowing how extensive the ore is, they need to build the infrastructure – roads, drainage equipment – and employ workers. *After* that expenditure, the lucky speculators find lead, silver, zinc, high quality copper ore, or even gold. If the yield is found to be poor, or the proportion of copper in the ore is low, there is a loss.

There are many sites scattered all over Wales where copper was mined or smelted but which were not that successful, or were considered nine-day wonders, and their history is known only within a localised area. Such ventures have their place in the history of the copper industry in Wales and cannot be omitted from the story.

Any investment involves an element of risk. So it proved to Morgan Hughes and partners in the 1820s when they invested their hard-earned money in the Derwen Deg Copper Mine venture in the Conwy Valley. They had, in January 1828, to explain how a sum of £415 had been spent at the mine. At the same time, a balance sheet for the mine was produced which had a rather curt note on the reverse side saying the copper was worth only £25! No wonder, then, that the mine was closed for the next forty-five years.

Lady Erskine leased the mine in September 1865 for twenty-one years at an annual rent of £10 to a group of businessmen, which included George Ingham, David Owen,

James Gibson Bradley and Robert Morris. By 1878 this company of men had given up their holding and the mine was leased by Walter Arnold Bradley and an associate to the Derwen Deg Pannol Gwyn Copper and Lead Mining Company. Based at the Baltic Building in Liverpool, the principal shareholder was R. W. Richardson; the company secretary was W. J. Richardson. The company did not have a long life. In 1881 they had left the mine, and a year later were in the hands of the liquidator. They had, to their credit, employed fourteen men in 1878, twenty-six in 1879 and thirty-three in 1880, which was a great help to the local economy when they were at work, but only 60 tons of copper was raised from the mine.

The next company to risk its money at Derwen Deg was the North Wales Freehold Copper Miners and Smelting Company. It saw the light of day on 23 July 1881 and had £250,000 to its name. The property it bought was a site of twenty-seven acres, sold by Henry Horatio Fanshawe for £130,000 on 23 September 1881. Matters got off to a bad start. Fanshawe and the board of directors of the company fell out because of an altercation about the distribution of shares. The mine, which had been described in glowing terms to prospectors, failed to live up to its description and was placed in the hands of the liquidators in 1882. The miners threatened not only to go on strike but to wreck the mine. There were, then, sixty-five men working at the mine, forty-three of them underground, who had in the space of three months raised 22 tons of ore. Managers H.B. Vercoe and D. Douglas managed to hold the fort until 31 March 1882. Unbelievably, another company, the Conway Valley Mining Company Limited, was formed on 30 June 1882 and stepped into the breach. One of its directors was W. A. Bradley, who had held 20,000 shares with the previous company. Another major shareholder in the new venture was Elizabeth C. Bradley, with 26,000 shares to her name. Their prospects appeared to be a little brighter when a new supply of ore was discovered by Captain Vercoe, but this new lode produced only 8 tons of copper ore, out of which was produced less than one ton of copper, worth £42.

In May 1888 yet another company, the Carnarvonshire Freehold Copper Mining Company Limited, actually thought of acquiring the Derwen Deg Mine. Thankfully the group of Liverpool speculators must have read an article in *Mining World*, which advised them not to. Nothing more came out of the mine.

Glasdir, in the Dolgellau gold-producing region, was firstly a copper mine. It was worked opencast, starting in about 1852. Between 1872 and 1914, 13,077 tons of dressed copper ore left the mine. In 1907 Stanley Elmore was involved at the Sygun Mine, Beddgelert. When that mine failed he moved much equipment from there to Glasdir, but the mine closed in 1915. Between 1872 and 1914, the output was 8,275 ounces of silver (1913–14) and 735 ounces of gold (1914).

Above Ganllwyd, again within the gold-belt, is the area known as Dolfrywnog. Here, in about one square mile of land in the Coed y Brenin forest, can be found over thirty different adits and shafts. These were mostly trial workings for copper and gold, made in the nineteenth century under a variety of names, although Dolfrwynog itself did record some production, including 167.25 ounces of gold from 311 tons of quartz between 1853 and 1865. These official figures are, however, a likely understatement: Hall (1992) quotes the secretary of the mine as having written later: 'During the old company's time we crushed 311 tons 1 cwt of quartz and obtained and sold therefrom 170 ozs 5 dwt 5 grains of gold. The above is a result of that only of which we kept record'.

Also within this area is the curious and apparently unique

Turf Copper Mine, where about 70 acres of peat bog were found to contain enough native copper to warrant it being stripped and either ashed on site in kilns, or sent directly to Swansea for smelting. At least 1,750 tons of copper ore were extracted during the first half of the nineteenth century; there are reports of large profits being made as early as 1810, although official figures are from 1824–1847.

The Turf Copper Mine was described in 1856 by W. J. Henwood:

> Some of the lowest portions of the upper peat-bed were so rich in copper, that they were carried to the Swansea smelting works in the condition in which they were extracted; some of the leaves are said to have been covered with a thin pellicle of bright metallic copper; nuts were coated in like manner, and on being broken afforded also a kernel of the same; and I was informed that the copper was in some cases deposited between the fibres of the wood; so that on being cut it exhibited alternate layers of vegetable matter and metal.

A. C. Ramsey, author of the Geological Survey of Great Britain 1866 wrote of it as being:

> In a hollow, about half a mile south and west of Moel Hafod-Owen. The drainage of the ground occupied by the greenstone and talcose schist runs into it, and the water percolating through the rocks and rising in springs, carried copper in solution from those specks and strings (of copper and iron sulphides) that are more or less diffused through the mass of the hills above. In this manner the peat mass appears to have been partly saturated with copper in the state of a soluble carbonate. The turf was pared from the surface and burnt in kilns,

and a large residue of valuable copper was afterwards separated from the ashes. Many thousand pounds' worth were thus extracted.[8]

Around the remains of the Coed y Brenin Turf Copper Mine can be seen pink Sea Thrift flowering in spring and summer. These plants are metal-tolerant, which is why they thrive here, away from their usual coastal habitat.

Ogof Wyddon (*ogof*: cave; *wyddon*: witch/warlock), Machynlleth Parc Copper Mine, is a Bronze Age site, dated by the Early Mines Research Group in 1998. It is said that the mine is haunted.

In 1856 Morris Williams was granted the rights to work the mine on condition that he pay to the owner, Sir Watkin Williams Wynn, a proportion of the ore that was brought to the surface. By May of that year Williams had started the work of draining the site with his partner Henry Weston of Machynlleth. They had more or less completed the work by September and while cutting a level found ores of copper, lead and silver. Weston formed a limited company and raised money by selling £2,000 worth of shares for a £1 each. He himself had shares numbered 1 to 220. By then he was also the works manager. Shares numbered 221 to 226 were owned by Lilia, Percy, Frank, Laura, Kate and Sophia Weston, who were all described as miners apart from Sophia, a 'spinster'. The remaining shares were held by nineteen others, including Morris Williams and David Jones who had thirty-one each by rights of discovery. By the start of 1857 it was found that they did not have enough money to continue and the works was abandoned.

Dylife, south east of Machynlleth, is better known as a lead mine, but was possibly worked for copper in pre-Roman and Roman times. It was also worked for periods during the eighteenth century, and from 1818 to 1891; from

1899 to 1901; and until the 1920s. It produced 1,540 tons of copper ore, 390 tons of zinc, 160,000 ounces of silver and 37,000 tons of lead.

Geufron Copper Mine is situated west of Llanidloes. It was definitely being worked during 1836 as this date has been carved into one of the walls of the main adit.

Llanymynech Ogof, in Llanymynech Hill, five miles south-west of Oswestry and straddling the Wales-England border, was once mined for copper, lead and zinc. Today, a golf course covers part of the hill. One entrance to the mine is called 'Yr Ogof'. During the Bronze Age there were two forts on the hill. Excavations have shown that copper smelting took place. Copper was mined here, in surface pits or hollows and later in underground passages. Bronze Age miners used antler and bone picks to get at the ore. The Romans used their own technology to work the mine. When the Romans left, the mine was not worked until the twelfth century, when a search for silver, lead and zinc took place. In the 1850s a mining company, with the help of a false report of an underground fortune, persuaded many local people to invest their money in the mine. After spending as little as was necessary to demonstrate some signs of activity, both directors and money disappeared.

Walter Davies (1761–1849), is also known by his bardic name of *Gwallter Mechain*. He was a well-educated man, having gained degrees from All Souls College, Oxford, and Trinity College, Cambridge. He was also a well-known poet, editor and clergyman. Whilst curate of Meifod, Montgomeryshire, he began a survey of the agriculture and economy of Wales, published in three different volumes in 1810 and 1815. Samuel Lewis' *Topographical Dictionary of Wales (1833)* has many contributions by Walter Davies.

Davies explored Llanymynech (or Ogof) mine in 1795. He found the whole face of the rock covered with calcareous incrustations slowly being converted into a substance similar to 'lac lunae' or mineral agaric. Having talked to many local people, he was quite familiar with the history of the mine and knew of several skeletons that had been found there in 1826. Culinary utensils, a fireplace, and a small axe were found near them. Nearby were Roman coins, suggesting that the other remains had been there since Roman times. One skeleton had a bracelet of glass beads around his left wrist and a battleaxe by his side, suggesting that he could have been a druid. About fifteen years later, other miners found more human bones in the mine, along with a gold wrist bracelet.

In 1877 John Fewtrell made the first accurate survey of the mine. The Reverend Elias Jones explored the mine in 1896. Others explored and visited the site during the twentieth century and complained of the smell of sheep inside the caverns, some of which are named Badger Chamber, Mandible Chamber, Shaft Chamber and Terminal Chamber. It is said that members of a local mining club found human bones in the mine, but possibly the most exciting discovery were the silver coins which fell from a rock inside the mine during a visit from some school pupils.

Carbon 14 dating has been used to prove that there are Bronze Age copper workings in Cardiganshire, especially on Copa Hill, Cwmystwyth. Many believe that Copa is a mispronunciation of the Welsh word for copper (*copr*) but it is not: it means the top of a hill or summit. The workings date from 2,100 BC. Cwmystwyth and Borth Bog have been investigated for Roman smelting remains. Later, copper mining in this area lost its importance to lead and silver mining.

Blaenceulan Mine, Talybont, Cardiganshire (Ceulanymaesmawr) was first worked about 1720. It was also worked in 1852 to 1855 and then in 1868 to 1876, with the final push made between 1878 and 1884. It supplied various ores, but never in any great quantities. In 1870, 438 tons of lead ore, 18 tons of copper ore and 7 tons of zinc ore were mined.

Castell Mine (Dyffryn Castell Mine; New Castell Mine; West Esgairlle Mine; Gwaithddu Mine; Cripiau Bach Mine), Ponterwyd, Cwm Rheidol, Ceredigion. Castell Mine was first opened by Thomas Bonsall in 1785 for sphalerite. It was closed by 1803, but was re-opened in 1850 and on eleven other occasions before the last period from 1916 to 1917. Records show that 5,365 tons of zinc ore, 139 tons of lead ore and 25 tons of copper ore were mined.

Dolclettwr Mine (Treddol Mine), Tre'r-ddol, Llangynfelyn, Ceregidion, was first worked in 1849 and was open until 1856. Only comparatively small quantities of ores were mined: 16 tons of lead ore; 147 tons of zinc ore; 80 tons of copper ore.

When the old mine at Cwmdaren Mine (Cwm Darren Mine; Lefel Gopor Mine; Copper Level Mine; Twll y Mwyn Mine), Penbontrhydybeddau, Trefeirig, Ceredigion, was re-opened in 1850, old tools were found, but they could not be dated to confirm that this was the remains of a Roman mine. They could easily have been from the seventeenth century. The mine's working life lasted until only 1856, when it was taken over by the owners of the Daren mine but was not worked. There were other attempts to work the mine in 1863. In 1920 the Twll y Mwyn section was investigated but nothing came of that venture. Cwmdaren Mine produced 21 tons of lead ore and 94 tons of copper ore in total.

Aberffrwdd Mine (Aberfrwdd Gothic Mine; East Aberffrwdd Mine; Aberffrwdd and Bonsall Mine; Gothic Mine), Devil's Bridge, Upper Llanfihangel-y-Creuddyn, Ceredigion, worked for a short period of three years in the

mid ninetenth.century, producing only 236 tons of lead ore
and 5 tons of copper ore.

Although both mines at Esgair Hir and Esgair Fraith,
Ceredigion, were worked together, it was from Esgair Fraith
that the copper ore was brought to the surface. The mine
was known to be working in 1691, and work continued until
1709. From 1851 to 1882 the mine worked as 'Cambrian',
and then as 'Esgair Fraith'. Until 1857 only lead was mined
at Esgair Fraith but by 1868, when it was closed, 700 tons of
copper ore had been mined. It is thought that up to 2,670
tons of copper ore were mined altogether.

Esgair Hir was the cause of controversy in 1692 when the
Crown claimed ownership from the Mines Royal, as the cost
of mining and smelting the silver ore was reportedly more
than the value of the silver. Sir Carbery Pryse claimed that
that the ore produced only a few pounds, while the Crown
agents held out that there were at least 60 pounds of the
metal.

Ystrad Einion Mine (Dolgoch Mine), Furnace, Ysgubor-
y-coed, Ceredigion, was another copper, lead and zinc-
producing mine which was first worked about 1700, for
another short time between 1745 and 1760, and for a very
short period of only a few months during 1853. In 1855 the
mine was working once more, as it did for short periods up
to 1901. Records of its output were kept only after 1845
(from that time mineral production figures had to be
furnished, by law): 9 tons of lead ore, 79 ounces of silver
(from 4 tons of lead ore), 10 tons of zinc ore and 45 tons of
copper ore. Today, the mine is better known for the remains
of a 16 foot underground waterwheel put in place by Mr
Adam Mason in 1871. Unfortunately parts of it (bearings)
were taken away by scrap merchants in 1910.

In the *History of the Cardiganshire Mines, from the Earliest
Ages, and Authenticated History to A.D. 1874, with their*

present position and prospects, Absalom Francis, Mining Agent, Engineer, and Surveyor, of Goginan, Aberystwyth wrote in 1874:

Tre'rddol Mine is situated about a quarter of a mile north of the village of the same name. It has been extensively worked at the surface and for some fathoms below an adit level, driven in from the mail road, leading from Aberystwith to Shrewsbury, and from it good quantities of blende and copper ores have been extracted. With the present price of blende ore, and with good machinery erected, which would cost from £2,000 to £3,000, the mine might be made to pay some profits, but in my opinion is never likely to become very remunerative or extensive.

Pwll Roman or Dolclettwr Mine is situated in the village of Taliesin about eight miles north-east of Aberystwith. This has been worked for more than a century near the surface, and about 30 years ago, under the name of Pwll Roman, received a good trial, which was made by a London company. The mine was sunk to about twenty fathoms under adit, and good and rich deposits of copper ore were found, in quantities, however that entailed a considerable loss on its working, and that company wound up their affairs sustaining a heavy loss.

It was again tried about fifteen years since by a Leeds company, and good copper raised, but a like result attended their efforts as those of the Pwll Roman Mine Company. It is now at work, and good copper and lead is being obtained from it. The character of the lode is good, and I am inclined to believe that if the engine shaft were sunk twenty fathoms deeper, and levels extended eastward, that good results would follow. To prove the mine thoroughly a capital of £5,000 should be raised.

Penybank and Erglwydd, in which there are three lodes, which all run into, and form a junction with the main lode of Penpompren. At these junctions good courses of lead and copper are found both on the Penpompren and the Penybank and Erglwydd lodes. These mines are very old ones, and have undoubtedly been worked, during different periods, for the last two hundred years. About thirty-five years ago, I recollect these workings, which were sunk about eleven fathoms under the adit level driven in northward from the south side of the hill, having been cleared and sunk on as far as the water would permit, without the aid of machinery. The vein is from six to eight feet wide, and is well filled with blended, copper, and lead ore, the matrix being a good gossan and crystallised spar.

Rare native copper (pure metal) has been found at Eaglebrook, Camdwrbach, Llechweddhelyg, Dolwen and Geufron, Llanidloes mines (where the date 1836 can be seen carved into one of the walls of the main adit) and Lodge Park copper trial near Tre'r-ddol, Ceredigion, in the Central Wales Orefield.

Talachddu Mine, Talachddu, Felin-fach, Breconshire (Powys) was a very isolated and small lead/copper mine which was worked in the early 1800s. The main geological curiosity of this mine is that it contains a north-south vein in Old Red Sandstone, an uncommon lode-bearing formation in the UK.

Penegarreg Mine, Tallyllychau, Carmarthenshire, was a small lead and copper mine near the village known by many as Talley, and was thus sometimes known as the Talley Mine. It was worked between 1854 and 1870 when 314 tons of lead ore and 54 tons of copper ore were sold. In 1879 the Llansawel Lead Mining Company was formed to take over the mine, to be followed by the Talley Mining Company in 1881. In the same year it was followed by the Penegarreg Silver-Lead Mining Company who continued to work it until 1892.

The Garn Copper Mine, Cydweli, Carmarthenshire, is on top of a ridge known as Mynydd y Garreg and was first mentioned in an agreement dated 1697 between Sir Humphrey Mackworth and William Waller of the Mine Adventurers. Waller took out a lease on the Garn mine at Cydweli for twenty-one years. Later, in October 1697, he also agreed to smelt the produce of the mine at the smelting works of Sir Humphrey Mackworth. Both men knew of each other, as Waller was the steward of the Esgair Hir mine. Waller was probably aware of the problems Mackworth was having in finding a plentiful supply of ore for his Melincryddan smelting mill.

Although it was better known as a supplier of limestone, a number of leases for the mining of copper and lead were issued in connection with the mine. In 1816 a Captain Nettles wrote of a very good trial at Garn but there were constant problems with flooding. From June to September 1816 work had to be stopped because rainwater flowed into the mine faster than it could be drained. Despite the problems, about 7 tons of concentrate was delivered to a Mr Parker's rooms.

Risca Copper Works (also known as Dan-y-graig Works) was one of two copper works in Monmouthshire (the other being Cwmavon, Torvaen Copper Works). Risca was established by the Union Company in 1807, but trade was so depressed in 1817 that the workers had to draw lots to decide which works were to be given up. Risca lost and the copper works was abandoned, to be converted and used as a chemical works. Another reason why the business folded was that the shareholders, who knew the ins and outs of the copper industry, found that they could buy copper cheaper from other sources than they could produce it themselves.

In his survey of Wales beginning north of the Dyfi (in central Wales, with its estuary at Aberdyfi), and ending south of the Tawe (which reaches the sea at Swansea), Walter Davies noted a number of copper mines at other sites:

At Cefn Maesmor, on the Montgomeryshire side of the brook Llyvnant.

Some copper ore is found in both the lead mines of Ynys Cynvelin, and Eurglawdd, near Tal-y-bont in Cardiganshire, both, worked by Mr Job Sheldon.

At Esgair Vraith, somewhat east of the Welsh Potosi silver mine [named after a Bolivian silver mine], a copper mine was discovered about the year 1693. So late as 1773, 20 tons of ore was raised and sold for 15/- a ton. In 1791 it sold for 25l-.

On a waste (common land), in the manor of Creuddyn, near Cwm Ystwyth lead mine, a great quantity of copper ore was formerly raised, though very little of late.

There are caves, hollow pits and banks of rubbish, at Caio, in Caermarthenshire, which discover there being some mine-works. In our opinion, if ever any kind of ore was raised at Caio, it was either of copper or lead.

At Llywernog were two mines – Nant Eos and on Gogerddan property.

Copper Hill – a great quantity of copper ore hath been raised here in former times, according to Mr Lewis Morris, but there is no great work carried out at present.

Mynydd Bach – some copper ore.

Copper ores, in other places, are so inconsiderable so as not to be worth mentioning.

---

[8] Mason and Bevins, *British Mining,* 71 (2002), 5–12.

The lives of the copper workers

18

A life in the day of a copper worker

When Benjamin Disraeli was prime minister he described the population of Great Britain as being of two different nations – the Poor and the Rich: 'They are like two nations that have no contact or sympathy. They know little of each other's habits, thoughts and feelings.' For those lucky enough to be rich, life was easy; for the poor, life was hard. The rich could easily afford to educate their children; the poor children went to 'the school of hard knocks'.

Children have always been used as a source of cheap labour, but this was especially so in Great Britain during the Industrial Revolution. Youngsters were exploited in almost all kinds of work situations, whether at home, on a farm or in factories, mines and other industrial establishments. They were regarded as smaller versions of adults, who could be taught useful crafts but paid lower wages for their efforts. Children worked long hours without complaint, but if they did voice their concerns, they could be easily disciplined – or sacked.

In 1842 an Act of Parliament was passed preventing women, young girls and children under the age of thirteen from working down the coal mines. This was considered to be a very enlightened Act. Previously, children as young as five years old had worked as fan operators in parts of coal mines too narrow for grown men to enter. The Act also brought to an end the practice of using women and girls to haul full drams (trucks) of coal to the surface. Though Robert Peel and his government were thought of as enlightened for passing such an Act they dared not go any further for fear of upsetting mine owners and losing the support of influential industrialists.

If the young women and children of the coal mines were spared hard manual work, it was not so for everyone. The rules were not half as relaxed in the copper industry. Hard work ruled, and much of it was done by women and children (boys and girls). The Copper Ladies of Parys Mountain were tough, and would boast that as they were used to hard work on the farm or at spinning the yarn, they could cope with anything they had to do on the mountain!

Hwy weithient oll yn galed
Am gyflog bychan iawn –
O'r braidd cant drigain ceiniog
Am weithio wythnos lawn.

[They all work hard
For a very small wage –
Earning only five shillings
For a full week's work.]

As we have already seen, the Census Returns between 1841 and 1901 show that many of the Copper Ladies were only children and young girls, with thirty-one of them being in their teens or even younger (Ellen Hughes of Tŷ Popty, Penygraigwen being the youngest at only eleven years of age) and twenty-five were in their twenties.

Similar statistics can be gleaned from details of the Swansea copper works, where, in 1842, fifty-four women and forty-seven girls under the age of thirteen, together with 314 boys and youths, worked at the Middle Bank, White Rock, Hafod and Morfa copper works. So many young females were employed in Swansea that an inquiry was called for by the Children's Employment Commission.

Evidence given showed that women and girls were

employed as barrow girls who had to wheel copper ore, coal and ashes to and from the furnaces. Such work had to be done in all kinds of weather and a shift lasted from six o'clock in the morning until two or three in the afternoon, by which time they had to build up enough stock of ore and coal to keep the furnaces going until the next morning. Boys of twelve would try and double their efforts so as to finish by dinner time, but if they slacked off to ease the pace their shift would last until as late as six o'clock in the evening. For all this they were paid four shillings a week (which was more than some of their contemporaries who worked in the pits could earn). The barrow boys were allowed half an hour for breakfast and an hour for their dinner, which was just enough time to cook and eat what they had brought: they used small ovens which had been built conveniently near the furnaces.

Despite what the owners thought, Rhys William Jones, Children's Employment Commissioner, was of the opinion that such work was far too strenuous for women and children and that the copper works were no fit places for them. One who gave evidence to the Commission was Elizabeth Matthew, who described her shift as being of nine hours' duration, during which she wheeled almost twenty-three tons of copper in 150 journeys, and at the end of which she would be far too tired to attend the evening service at her local church.

Benjamin Pollard of Park Street, St Mary's, Swansea, was a forty-year-old agent at the Morfa Copper Works. He testified that children brought up to labour in this way were much better at their job than those who started at a later age, and that they worked because their parents wanted it so. This was difficult for the Commissioner to understand as he knew that a furnaceman earned about twenty-five shillings a week, which was more than other skilled workers. The extra money coming into the house was used to buy beer: the heat a furnaceman faced at work when skimming off the slag in the furnace would cause him to sweat profusely, after which he would drink a jug of cold water and at least two pints of beer.

Those who lived at St David's in Pembrokeshire and worked at Treginnis would leave the house at 6 a.m. to start their long day of labour. Miners such as John Reynolds, who lived in Solva, would have had to start a twelve-mile walk to work as soon as possible after 4 a.m. to be there on time. He died young, as the result of an accident.

Boys were not allowed to work in front of the furnaces. It took years before they were pronounced proficient enough to do the work and strong enough to withstand the heat. They were put to work when they were between thirteen and sixteen years old, looking after the calciners in which copper ore was burnt to rid it of the excess of sulphur. A barrow-full of ore would be wheeled on staging to the top of the furnace and tipped into the furnace. Their shift would be a double one of twenty-four hours, from six one morning until six the next. As they had to tend the furnace every two hours, a prolonged sleep was out of the question, so they made do with catnaps and were woken by the night-watchmen. Once a fortnight a 'long watch' was worked so as to change their working days – this meant that they worked non-stop for forty-eight hours from Saturday until Monday morning. Despite their youth, they were experienced enough to realise that they could not work such a shift without a proper break, so they paid someone else to take their place during the two nights of the very 'long watch'. Local doctors were pleasantly surprised at how healthy the youngsters were, despite the arduous conditions in which they worked. They suffered very few injuries, but the effects of the smoke and sulphur, the heat and extreme changes of temperatures, did affect their lungs. One young worker had been forced to look for 'light duties' when he was only fifteen.

Work conditions were similar in the copper mines, with hard work, long hours and low wages common for all. These hardships had their effects: copper workers were quite easy to spot in a crowd, because they looked about ten or fifteen years older than those who worked in agriculture or other professions.

19

Copper works schools

Robert Owen, the social reformer from Newtown in Powys, was an elected member of the Literary and Philosophical Society of Manchester. On 29 December 1793 he read a paper at the society's meeting entitled *The Usefulness of Education*. He had realised the value of an education to the poor in general and to his workers in particular. He was convinced that education was important in developing the type of person he wanted in his workplace but also as members of society – good, humane and rational.

In 1799 he arrived at New Lanark, Lanarkshire, Scotland, to take charge of the cotton mills. By 1800 there were up to 2,000 mill workers in New Lanark with about 500 apprenticed children. Some of them were as young as six or seven, and everyone, whether old or young, worked from six in the morning until seven at night. At the end of the working day, there was half an hour of compulsory education for the children. His school curriculum included music, dancing and nature study. His teachers were instructed to teach order; to train the pupils to act and think rationally, and to encourage the pupils to ask questions. More than once, Robert Owen made clear that the prime vehicle for the type of social reform he hoped for was education.

Owen had a keen interest in education and its benefits. He donated quite large sums of money to help establish schools, and with the help of his partners in New Lanark built a school for the mill workers' children. His example spread to other mill and works owners, but unfortunately his ideas did not penetrate to all parts of Wales.

For many years the children of the Parys Mountain copper workers were left to their own devices rather than led to the learning troughs of education. Few people showed a real interest in children. The first names mentioned as providing an education for Amlwch children were Mr Edward and Mrs Eleanor Kynnier who, in 1689, left money to be invested on their behalf. Of the interest, two thirds was to be used for the benefit of the boys and a third for the girls. In time, the charity was forgotten and it wasn't until eighty-four years later that Thomas Williams (*Twm Chwarae Teg*) showed the caring side of his character when he helped the Amlwch Church Vestry to recover £311, 'the charity money left by Mr Edward and Mrs Eleanor Kynnier for the support of the schools'[1] at Amlwch. All these details were recorded in the Vestry Books on 30 December 1773.

In 1771 the Reverend Richard Owen, curate, made an application to Madam Bevan for a Circulating School to be set up in Amlwch. He was of the opinion that Amlwch was a dark and ignorant place where few parents sent their children to school because they preferred to send them to work in the mines to earn a few pennies a week.

A public meeting was held in Amlwch on 6 April 1818 to discuss establishing a National School. It was decided to write to the Plas Newydd family to ask for land on which to build the school. Another letter inviting financial support was sent to the Mona and Parys Mine companies, both of which donated £100 to the cause and promised to pay £25 annually towards the maintenance of the school when built and in use. Interest of £200 from the Kynnier Charity was donated to the fund to ease the financial pressure, but many problems had to be faced and the project was not completed until January 1824. Many of the parents were so poor that only a few could afford to pay the fees and the school always suffered a shortage of books and pencils and from the standard of teaching. In 1831 the teacher was condemned as a 'brute'.

A British School was opened in the neighbouring village of Rhosybol in 1844 'within reach of the vast population employed upon the Parys copper mines'.[2] The much-maligned Blue Books Report on the State of Education in Wales in 1846 gives a very disturbing view of education in Amlwch. According to Reverend William Roberts, Calvinistic Methodist minister, 'There are great numbers of children in Amlwch who receive no instruction, either on weekdays or on the Sunday. I think there is not a place in the country where there are so many children uneducated. I am sure there are hundreds in Amlwch.'[3] Another comment by a layman was that of Mr Samuel Greathead, Banker: 'There is a great deal of extreme poverty in this place. They have no clothes in which to send their children to school.'[4]

The inspector found that out of 250 children only 160 were present on the day of the inspection on 13 November 1847. Many of them, including some as young as seven and eight years old, were still being sent to work in the mines rather than to school. The floors, walls, windows and furniture were dirty, and the rooms were never washed or swept. In reading and writing considerable progress had been made, but in arithmetic they were very backward: 'There was not a child present able to work a sum in Proportion, or even in compound rules. No history or geography was taught.'

Robert Roberts took up his teaching post at Amlwch in 1855. He said that if he had read the Blue Books Report and seen the children beforehand, 'I think that I should not have entertained the thought of coming among them, even for a limited time.' He had the shock of his life, for 'when the school door was opened in the morning in rushed a crowd of boys such as I never saw except in the gutter. Half of them

had no shoes or stockings and most of them appeared not to
have seen soap and water for quite a while. They were as
unruly as wild horses and none of the local boys knew or
understood English.' These were not the observations of an
embittered man but an honest opinion that merely
confirmed a great deal of what had been said in the Blue
Books.[5]

Standards did not improve. There were Sunday Schools
but they were poorly attended. In 1853 it was suggested that
the teacher would be far better employed as a clerk at the
Mona Mine Offices. On 26 March 1860 a British School was
opened on land donated by William Jones of Dwygyfylchi,
Caernarfonshire, at a cost of £2,500. A grant of £1,146 was
also obtained.

Education in Amlwch had been very dependent on the
goodwill of a few charitable persons. A Ragged School was
opened and flourished between 1850 and 1870. Another
was founded by Mr and Mrs Morgan in 1887. A Voluntary
School had been set up in Amlwch Port in 1872 at a cost of
£340. Between 1763, when Robert Hughes (*Robin Ddu o
Fôn*) opened a school in the town, and 1890, a total of
twenty-six other schools were opened in Amlwch. Some
offered a classical, commercial or navigational education.
Others catered for young ladies and gentlemen. One private
school offered a course of Arithmetic for a fee of three
shillings a quarter, whilst another, run by W. Gregson of
Glanrafon, offered board and an education for £20 per
annum. In the same period four 'Dame Schools' and one
other school were opened in Amlwch Port. Many of the
founders' names showed that they were not local people:
Andrew, Clarke, Hobday, Kennedy, Larkin, Sellers, Skelton
and Treweek.

When the Macclesfield Company mined ore for the
Llandudno Mine Company it was a period of plenty. Men

found work, wages were regular, families were fed and everyone looked to a brighter future. The miners established schools on the Orme at Pen y Buarth and Tŷ Coch, and the schoolmaster was paid an annual salary of £30. Dr John Prichard, a Baptist minister, remembered that when he was about fourteen or fifteen, an English school came to Llandudno, maintained mainly by the proprietors of the mine. The schoolmaster was John Rees. There he started to learn English. Sometimes he attended school all day, sometimes in the afternoons having returned from his 'stems' in the mine, but not regularly. Before John Rees, the schoolmaster left, Pritchard could read a little of the Bible, and also write a little. John Rees' departure from Llandudno in 1811 meant that there would be no more schooling for John Pritchard and many others.

A feature of education in South Wales during the nineteenth century was that very successful copper works schools were set up and maintained by industrialists and works owners. One of the earliest was founded by Sir Humphrey Mackworth, who had been associated with works charity schools in north Cardiganshire. But the scale and size of the copper smelting industry in the Tawe Valley near Swansea meant that a much more organized system of schools was needed to fulfil the needs of a population that had been 6,099 in 1801, but had increased to 40,000 by 1851. The Vivian family of Swansea and the Nevills of Llanelli were among the leaders in the field of establishing such schools, though the very first copper works school was established in Swansea in 1806 by Pascoe St Leger Grenfell and John Freeman. This was a co-educational school for which the workmen of the White Rock, Upper and Middle Bank Copper Companies paid 1d per week from their wages. Girls who were admitted as pupils had to pay their own fees at the Works Office.

Llanelli schools had a noble benefactor in Charles Nevill of Birmingham. In 1804 Nevill, then a copper smelter in Swansea, set up a partnership with other copper smelters in Llanelli, which became the foundation of smelting and industrial development in the area. He also established schools for his workers' children. At the time Dame and Private Schools were offering an education at a price that ordinary workers could not afford, but a British or a National School had not been as yet established in the town to satisfy the needs of a rapidly growing population.

Nevill gave evidence to the Commissioners for Education in 1846 emphasising the need for an improved educational system in Llanelli. He was already involved in setting up schools of his own for the benefit of his workers. A school was held in the barracks of the Works' Yard and by 1847 classrooms had been built for infants and boys. Teachers' houses were added, and in January 1852 girls were admitted for the first time. Fees were collected on a weekly basis from parents and pupils, and those whose parents did not work for the company paid 1d a week extra.

The school was highly commended for its work under the leadership of David Williams (head teacher from 1847 to 1863). The school was again regularly praised under his successor J. E. Jones, because Llanelli Heolfawr School was the only school in Wales to teach practical and inorganic chemistry. Navigation was another useful subject: the company had its own ships, and local boys with their minds set on going to sea and studying for their Mate and Master's tickets benefited a great deal.

Another member of the Nevill family – W. H. Nevill – was one of the founders of Llangennech Village National School on the Gower. Along with C. W. and R. T. Nevill, he worked in the field of education. Their efforts, RT's in particular, were honoured when the Nevill Memorial Hall in

Llanelli was opened with a suitable eulogy to his work.

At Pembrey, in 1846, a copper works was built by a Birmingham/London consortium – Messrs Mason & Elkington. By 1855 the need for a school for the workers' children had become apparent. The company built a non-denominational school at a cost of £1,700 and also paid £270 for its maintenance. Workers paid a weekly fee for the school. Girls and boys were charged 1d or 2d a week, and infants 1d a week. Children of parents not employed at the works had to pay 1½d or 3d a week. Children of parents who earned less than £1 a week received free education. Attending this school did not guarantee a placement at the copper works later in life, a fact which meant that many 'outsiders' were admitted. In 1868 there were 265 'outsiders' on the roll and 214 'insiders', making a total number of 479 pupils on the register.

It is likely that without Pascoe Grenfell's efforts there would have been no school east of the Tawe in the period 1800–1850. His first school was built in 1806, but the building was small and the head teacher, a former mason, was not the best at conveying an education to his pupils. John Freeman donated a parcel of land in 1839 on which Pascoe Grenfell built the Kilvey Infants Copper Works School, with room for up to 200 pupils. Grenfell's schools were enlarged in 1850 to accommodate pupils from the St Thomas and Pentrechwyth areas. They also catered for pupils whose parents were not employed by the Company but were able to afford the slightly higher fee.

Grenfell was renowned for employing properly trained teachers, such as Richard Gwynne (1822–1907). Gwynne began his working life as a compositor but in 1841 trained at Grays Inn Road Model School and Norwood to become a teacher. His career began at the Kilvey Infants School but later he became headmaster of Kilvey Copperwork School, a post he held until 1892. He married Charlotte Lloyd of Kilvey, at Kilvey Church, in the parish of Llansamlet on 26 December 1857. They had a family of five sons (on whose education he spent all his savings) and one daughter. Richard Gwynne was a keen geologist and historian and was vice-president of the Royal Institution of South Wales for forty years. He died on 28 November 1908 and was buried in Oystermouth Cemetery.

One of Richard and Charlotte's sons, Howell Arthur Gwynne, became the editor of the *Morning Post* from 1911 to 1937. He died aged eighty-five on 27 June 1950. Another son, Dr Llewelyn Henry Gwynne (1863–1957) became Bishop of Khartoum.

Pascoe Grenfell also arranged annual inspections and successfully applied to the Committee of the Privy Council for extra funds and grants for salaries, teacher and pupil-teacher training, and for buying equipment. His schools were also non-denominational.

Despite Grenfell and Freeman's charitable and laudable ideas, not everyone was supportive of their work, and some leading ministers of religion of the time were critical of them, but Grenfell was determined to forge ahead – and especially so after he learnt of five young men who had been looking for work but could only make their mark on a piece of paper when it came to writing their names. He then made it a condition that everyone who was employed at his works should be able to read and write.

Mary, daughter of Pascoe Grenfell, showed the same interest as her father in education, and opened The Golden Griffin, a coffee house, where members of the public were educated about the evils of strong drink.

Other copper works schools were opened by the Vivians of Trevivian (Hafod). Established in specially-built premises, like the Kilvey schools, they were considered as model schools where a very high standard of education was taught. Regular praise from factory and school inspectors was a feature of their reports.

When the Vivians took over the Taibach Copper Works in 1839, they also took over the school that had been established by the English Copper Company. J. H. Vivian and his wife had a longstanding interest in education, were very conscious of the lack of educational facilities in Swansea, and were prominent in their support of the Reverend E. B. Squire, vicar of Swansea, who worked hard promoting the ideals of a National School in Swansea. Mrs Sarah Vivian took responsibility for a school for forty girls from the parish of St. John in 1823 and converted the Swiss Cottage and opened a Model Dame School in the grounds of Singleton Park for twenty-five boys and girls.

A motto of J. H. Vivian was that the key to industrial efficiency was a literate and numerate workforce. With this in mind he mixed with people who had already established schools for their employees, such as Sir John Guest at Dowlais Iron Works. With his background and interest in education, he opened the Hafod Copper Works Schools in February 1847. So many pupils attended that the buildings had to be extended. Within twelve months an Infants Department had to be built. The teachers had been trained in the Pestalozzi method, in which children learn through activity and through objects, and are free to pursue their own interests and to draw their own conclusions. In the two years 1846–1848 the Vivians built schools and playgrounds for 600 children at Trevivian.

Workers' children did not have to pay, but their parents contributed a fee of 1d per week which was deducted from their wages. Non-company children were charged up to 2d per week. Children from Pontarddulais, Llangyfelach, Birchgrove, Sketty and Cockett were admitted to the school. Walter Hogg, of the class of 1852, left and became a schools inspector. Between 1847 and 1854 Hafod schools were dependent on the school fees to purchase equipment and on subsidies from J. H. Vivian for salaries.

As in Amlwch, many of the boys were drawn to the works rather than the school and irregular attendance was a feature of many who much preferred a wage packet in their pockets than knowledge in their heads. For those who showed genuine progress and a love of learning, evening classes were arranged.

In general copper works schools proved effective and popular. Attendances were high. When the Hafod School first opened in 1847 the number of pupils on its roll was 350. By 1865 it had risen to 521 and in 1894 there were 1,114 on the roll and an average daily attendance of 889 (79.8 per cent). 'Excellent' was a prominent adjective in any official document and report about the school, which was always highly placed in the table of best performing schools in Wales. Vivian also supported the Court Herbert Colliery School in Skewen and the Sketty National School.

The Margam Copper Works School for Boys and Girls was established at Taibach in 1830 by the Margam Copper Works Company, whose patron was the Hon. Captain Lindsay, but it was taken over and managed by Pendarves Vivian of Swansea. Its Infants Department was very highly thought of, and many pupils found the education they had received helped them to better things than smelting work.

Another short-lived school was the Crown Copper Spelter Works School in Neath. This was a small school mentioned only once in the Reports of 1847 but listed afterwards as a private day school run in Cadoxton, Neath, by Miss Williams, with room for thirty pupils.

Whilst the education received at the Copper Schools was undoubtedly good, one must note that the Welsh language was not given its rightful place in the curriculum. At the time it was not considered the language of progress.

Due to many new industrial developments and processes, new inventions, the increasing use of complex machinery, there was a need for a literate, numerate upper working class. Education was crucial. Works owners and the sons of many owners had had a university education. Some were even educated abroad. Welsh did not feature highly on the curriculum of the period. Many of the Welsh-born gentry did not speak Welsh. Most of their workers could not afford a formal education, and relied on the Sunday schools to give them, in their own language, the skills they needed to survive. Many giants of Welsh culture emerged from those difficult times.

However, many industrialists wished their workers to be educated in English, and set out to achieve this.

---

[1] *Two Centuries of Anglesey Schools 1700–1902.* D. A. Pretty. (Anglesey Antiquarian Society, 1977).

[2] *Reports of the commissioners of enquiry into the state of education in Wales (1847).*

[3] *Ibid.*

[4] *Ibid.*

[5] *A Wandering Scholar: the Life and Opinions of Robert Roberts.* J. Burnett and H. G. Williams (eds.). (University of Wales Press, 1991).

20

Medical matters and troublesome smoke

In any heavy industry or large works, some dangers have to be faced. The ones which copper miners and smelters had to contend with ranged from minor accidents to fatal injuries. Loss of sight in a gunpowder explosion was a fairly common occurrence, as were broken bones, which resulted in arthritis later in life. Rupture or abdominal hernia was a common complaint; the more elderly workers at Parys Mountain were sent to work at the Precipitation Pits if suffering from the complaint as it was believed that the work was a little easier for them there than working in the mine.

Today Health & Safety Regulations make lives easier, but in pre-H&S days, before a proper medical service had been introduced, some of the mine and smelter owners have to be praised for their efforts in easing sufferers' pain. The Marquis of Anglesey cared for the Parys Mine Company's workers to the extent that the company paid a pension of 1/6d per week to the old and incapable Copper Ladies. The company also employed a doctor to care for the sick and injured. It has to be asked, though, how efficient was such a doctor if he lived over fifty miles away in Dolgellau. Following a tragedy at the works in 1785, when forty men were killed, the surgeon Griffith Roberts had to travel all the way to Anglesey from Merionethshire to tend the injured. For his troubles he was paid an annual salary of £300.

A young boy whose father had been killed at the mine, and who worked for nine pence per day, applied for compensation as he had no clothes because 'work at the kilns burns more clothes than any other branch belonging to the mines'.[1] It is not known whether or not this 1817 application was successful.

In the same year Owen Ellis, a 77-year-old man who had worked at the mines for thirty-eight years, was successful in his application for a pension. The mine owners granted him a sum of four shillings per week due to his long service – his gain was also a loss, though, for he lost the shilling per week that the parish paid him.

In 1817 a total of 102 applications were received, but only twenty-four were granted. A miner who was already blind in one eye, and had suffered a broken leg and ribs in an accident, was refused a claim for compensation and a pension.

Gabriel Owen, forty-six years old, a blind and deformed worker who had been at the mine for twenty-seven years, was granted a pension of two shillings per week to support his wife and five children as he was not in receipt of any parish relief.

Robert Williams, with forty years' service at the mine to his name, was another who was granted 3 shillings per week pension, but as he had been receiving 2 shillings per week from the parish, he was only a shilling a week better off.

Letters were sent to the Marquis appealing for a pension on behalf of injured workers. Cornelius Pritchard of Twrllachiad, a Methodist chapel elder who could read and write both in Welsh and English, was Land Agent for the Llys Dulas family. He was one person who wrote on behalf of many. He was considered by many of the miners as an angel of mercy, but was considered a cheat and a liar by others and also as one who was determined to create trouble and unrest at the mine.

Other rejected applications included that of Cornelius Solomon, eighty years old, who had worked for the Mona Mine Company for nineteen years. His plea was refused, whilst Owen Ellis, seventy-seven years old, who had worked for the company for eighteen years, was awarded a pension of 4 shillings per week.

One letter of appeal to the Marquis was on behalf of William Jones:

Amlwch
1 January 1866

Dear Sir,
I beg most humbly to suggest for your consideration my pitiful condition being 77 years of age and having served Lord Anglesey at the Smelting Works uninterruptedly except in time of sickness for the space of 46 years I earnestly hope that his Lordship will please to allow me a small pension for the remainder of my days which at most will be but very few

And his petitioner will ever pray

Your most humble servant
William Jones.'[2]

In 1817, a ballot was held amongst the Parys Mountain workers to elect a works doctor. There were four candidates. Dr Roose won narrowly, with 157 votes, against Dr R. Jones with 146. Some of the voters believed it had been a mock election and that the winner was given the post because he was related to the mine agent Stephen Roose, a fact that James Treweek had to deny publicly.

Dr Roose was elected again in 1821. To take advantage of his services miners had to pay 2d per week.

By January 1831 there was a choice of three works doctors who could be called upon in the event of an accident. A complaint was made against all three in February of that year: the workers had lost confidence in their skills and bedside manners, and the drunken one (not named) was certainly not welcome in the works. A further complaint was that a fee had to be paid to Mr Roose and Mr

Williams (surgeons), whether their patients were injured or not. Later that year Dr Webster, the assaying official's son, set himself up as a town doctor in Amlwch . The workers were permitted to ask for his services in the case of an accident, though the weekly medical dues had to be paid whether they used the works doctor or not.

From 1845 onwards the mine workers were allowed to choose which doctor they preferred to attend to them, and the company paid the cost. A personal donation from the Marquis covered the expense of a hospital visit to Bangor, Chester or Liverpool, and compensation of four or five shillings per week whilst they were in hospital. Later still it was agreed that the mine workers had the right to call for the service of any doctor if needed, without having to worry about payment.

In about 1860 a number of young men were newly employed in the mine and the old and infirm were consequently excluded from work without any payment. A number of applications for a long-service pension were made. Both Dr Thomas Hughes of the Parys Mine Company and Dr Richard Lewis Parry of the Mona Mine Company testified to a Royal Commission in 1863 that the average wage in the mine was fourteen shillings per week. It was a very difficult period for all and the circumstances at the mine were not at all healthy, with a strong smell of cordite hanging in the air for almost two hours after every explosion. The workers had no choice but to breathe the foul air and suffer the consequences. Many suffered from the dust or contracted tuberculosis as they cut and blasted through layers of quartz and silica rock to get at the copper ore. Another constant danger was breathing the toxic sulphuric acid fumes from the smelting fires. Very many suffered from arthritis. Some even had their own cures: for example, an ounce of gunpowder mixed in a pint of spiced ale to relieve aching joints. Others suffered from bad digestion because they drank so much boiling hot coffee or tea to relieve other symptoms. As previously noted, both doctors were agreed that Parys Mountain workers had the appearance of men at least fifteen years older than those of the same age who worked in agriculture.

A small hospital – the Dinorben Hospital – was opened in Amlwch in 1872, paid for by a donation of £600 by Lady Dinorben of Llys Dulas. According to Worrall's Directory (1874):

It is run on the cottage principle and has been open about twelve months. It is well adapted for the purpose, being beautifully situated on the road to Bull Bay; it is supported by voluntary subscriptions.

Honorary Medical Officer, T. Hughes, Esq., M.D.

Honorary Treasurer and Secretary, Mr John Lewis

The hospital was closed in 1893.

In Swansea in 1865 a Yellow Fever epidemic broke out. Yellow fever is a serious and sometimes fatal viral infection that is transmitted by mosquitoes. Symptoms include high temperature, internal bleeding, kidney failure and even meningitis. Hepatitis causes yellow colouring of the skin (jaundice). Yellow fever can become an epidemic, with a mortality rate of around 50 per cent. The virus is introduced into the bloodstream via the saliva of the mosquito *Aedes egyptii* as it bites. Despite the fact that the *Aedes egyptii* mosquito is found in Asia, Yellow Fever normally occurs only in Africa and South America, but when it reached Swansea it caused an epidemic and panic.

Wales had suffered from cholera epidemics. The first occurred in 1831. A local health board was established with the intention of cleaning the town's streets, washing the houses with lime, and organising the distribution of clean clothes for the poor. Amlwch suffered three cholera epidemics by 1866. The third and last was brought to Holyhead by ship and to Amlwch by a Dublin ship.

A virulent influenza epidemic hit Anglesey in 1890, but cholera and influenza were comparatively easy to treat. Ships entering the ports of Beaumaris or Holyhead were required to hang a yellow quarantine flag if one or more of the crew members were infected, but no such flag was seen flying from the top mast of the *Hecla* when she arrived in Swansea at 9.00 a.m. on Saturday, 9 September 1865. She was carrying not only a cargo of Cuban copper ore, but also the deadly Yellow Fever.

The barque *Hecla*, captained by William Clouston, was a wooden sailing vessel which had left Cuba for Swansea with a cargo of copper ore on 26 July 1865. George Wilson, the ship's boy, had already died from Yellow Fever; another crew member, Hansel Pederson, was left suffering in hospital. Of the remaining four officers, ten seamen and two passengers who were on board, three (of the crew) were buried at sea, their deaths recorded as being due to Yellow Fever. By the time of the ship's arrival in Swansea two others who had suffered from the fever were recovering. A sixth, James Saunders, had fallen ill on the 27 August. Despite knowing all this the master did not have a yellow quarantine flag flying from the mast when he picked up George Morgan, a Bristol Channel pilot, and extra crew members. Saunders, who was thought to be suffering from dropsy, was lowered over the side and taken to a lodging house where he was seen by three doctors, all of whom recognised Yellow Fever symptoms. Saunders was also visited by the town mayor, just three hours before dying.

As well as the copper ore, the *Hecla* had also

inadvertently carried infected mosquitoes to Swansea. Before unloading began on 13 September the passengers and remainder of the crew of the *Hecla* had left the ship and gone their separate ways. Questions were asked about Saunders' death and what exactly had happened to the others on board the ship. A series of public health measures were quickly put into effect. Saunders, wrapped in a tarred shroud, was buried as soon as possible and his bedding and clothing were destroyed. The room in which he died had to be disinfected with lime wash and chloride of lime. The Swansea Sanitary Inspector and a Mr Evans, lecturer in chemistry at the Normal College in Swansea, were sent to fumigate with chlorine the 'clothes, rooms and persons' of the passengers and crew of the *Hecla*, who had been located by the police. Unloading of the ship was stopped on the afternoon of her arrival; she was closed up, and 'purified' with chloride of lime for the next three days. Unloading was restarted on 13 September and was finished by 21 September.

A rigger from a nearby vessel *Eleanor* went on board the *Hecla* and six days later (on the 15th) he was diagnosed as suffering from Yellow Fever. Thankfully, he recovered. A local customs officer died. The outbreak then developed into an epidemic. At least twenty-seven people were infected and fifteen died. Another seven were diagnosed as showing strong symptoms of the fever, but none of those died.

During the epidemic 'almost tropical heat prevailed at Swansea',[3] with a daytime temperature in excess of 21 degrees Celsius. This closely resembled the conditions at Santiago de Cuba, providing perfect conditions for mosquitoes, which had bitten the sufferers.

Such were conditions in Santiago de Cuba, and so many Swansea sailors died there, that the place was given the morbid nickname of 'Swansea cemetery'. In January 1845 twelve Swansea ships sailing back home from Cuba lost at least one crew member to Yellow Fever. *The Lady Pirie* lost five or six.

Other cases of Yellow Fever were recorded in Swansea in 1843, 1851 and 1864, but thankfully not on an epidemic scale.

Smoke from the copper works was a big problem. The copper ores that were smelted in Swansea were very impure, and needed to be roasted and melted several times to eradicate all the impurities. Separating the metal from the ore produced slag and ashes, leading to arsenical and sulphurous clouds hanging over the smelting works or driven across country by the prevailing winds.

Thomas Pennant was not impressed when he saw, smelt and breathed 'Suffocating fumes of burning heaps of copper arise in all parts, and extend their baneful influence for miles around.'

Early attempts at smelting ores in Holywell led to poisonous fumes having a detrimental effect on the locality. The works of Samuel Flete, built in 1590, and Madam Kaye (1733) were closed down after public protests. Poisoned smoke from Flete's works contaminated the water and killed most of the animals and fish; fumes from Madam Kaye's lead smelting, on land leased from Roger Pennant of Downing, Whitford, killed the vegetation on land belonging to the Mostyn family.

Many early descriptions of Swansea contain references to the smoke. The *Tour of Gower* was published in 1859 by G. P. Bevan of London. He says:

coming over the viaduct at Landore one gets a pretty good notion of what the copper works are like outwardly.

How people can exist in this pandemonium seems a mystery, but not only do they exist, but according to Dr Thomas Williams' report, they are actually healthy and attain a tolerably long life.

He goes on to say that 'the population is large and rather dirty towards the upper part of the town in which the railway station is situate, but improves towards the west, where aristocratic Swansea principally resides.'

It must have been a very difficult task for any author to find something positive to say about Swansea. Wirt Sikes tried his best in 1883:

The copper-smoke cloud which hangs over a part of Swansea, and which blasts the vegetation over which it hangs, while not an addition to the attractions which draw the eye, is the banner of its commercial prosperity.[4]

His next paragraph includes a further explanation:

The town is indeed the copper metropolis of the queendom. Copper smelting was introduced here as early as 1090, when the ore was brought over in boats from Cornwall and Devon, but now ores come from every part of the world.[5]

The Reverend H. Elvet Lewis of Llanelli, said in 1892 that Swansea did 'not smile on its incoming visitors: they have to enter the town from the outside world through the chronic smoke of Landore, which spoils the landscape, but means bread and home to thousands of people.'[6] Nothing much had changed in the thirty years since George Borrow's visit: he had described the town as being, 'a large, bustling, dirty, gloomy place', where he found very little apart from 'immense stacks of chimneys surrounded by grimy diabolical looking buildings, in the neighbourhood of which were huge heaps of cinders and black rubbish. From the chimneys smoke was proceeding in volumes, choking the atmosphere all around.'[7]

In the mid nineteenth century, seventeen of the eighteen copper works in Britain were located in Wales, and almost half of those were in the Swansea area. The people of Swansea were very displeased, so much so that the 'The South Wales copper-smoke dispute' lasted from 1833 until 1895.

The gentrified owners of the copper works built their houses and lived to the west of the town, such as at Singleton Park (John Henry and Richard Hussey Vivian's shared house) which was clear of the smoke. The people who worked the smelters, and their families, had to make do with small terraced houses close to the works.

A note written by John Place, manager to the Mines Royal Company, on 26 December 1796, states that Lady Mackworth had objected to signing a lease, as she thought the copper smoke would affect the Gnoll House. Whilst Sarah Vivian could grow exotic plants in her gardens, poor 'Mrs. Jones' from Trevivian couldn't grow anything except copper potatoes and cabbages whose leaves turned to dust when touched. Working-class people were reluctant to complain as the smelters offered them their only constant source of employment. If the works were closed to completely eradicate the smoke they would have cut off their noses to spite their faces. Which way were they to turn?

But there is only so much that a person can take. In 1820 Mansel Phillips, High Sheriff of Glamorgan, a landowner and one who could well afford to pay for solicitors and lawyers, reached breaking point. He took the Vivian Copper Works masters to court, as he considered the smoke from the works a 'common nuisance'. Such a case was considered a threat to the prosperity of Swansea, so the matter was dealt with in Cardiff. The Vivians explained that it was their intention to find a solution to the problem. Phillips did not take the matter any further.

This was only the start of an issue which would drag on for over sixty years. Phillips had to reduce his rents on some of his properties as the tenants complained of the effects of the smoke. The Vivians acknowledged that this was an unsatisfactory situation, but said that should they yield to one worker it would open the floodgates to a myriad of others to make claims against them.

John Henry Vivian, to placate his fellow men, was very supportive of the Royal Institution of South Wales, which suggested that a competition be held to 'devise a method for removing the destructive gases'.[8] He put forward a prize of £1,000 to whoever could satisfy a panel of adjudicators that his or her solution was successful in factory conditions. Another stipulation was that the remedy to the problem had to be seen to be working within six months of the opening date of the competition.

The competitors were Bevington Gibbins from Swansea; John Henry Vivian, also a Swansea man; William Weston Young from Neath; William Williams, who had plans drawn up but submitted no details for his experiments; and W. Hills, who had a scheme, which was considered by the adjudicators as useless.

Gibbins and Vivian were copper smelters. Young's background was more varied. He had been a surveyor, false teeth maker, a designer of tombs and harbours and a painter of fine china in Nantgarw and Swansea. Gibbins conducted his experiments at the Rose Works in Swansea; Vivian conducted his at the Hafod Works. Young worked on open ground near Neath.

Vivian relied on the expertise and knowledge of others such as Michael Faraday, Sir Humphrey Davy and Professor Richard Phillips and conducted his experiments in August 1821. He was quite pleased with the results, but he spent almost £3,000 on the exercise.

. Weston Young complained that the adjudicators had not given his work adequate attention but they had satisfied themselves that his methods could not eradicate the smoke.

Neither Young nor Vivian had satisfied the panel that they were completely successful as sulphurous acid gas was still present in the air, so both of them were denied the laurels of victory.

Vivian continued to make use of what he had prepared for the competition. Huge chimney stacks were built and used at the Hafod Works until 1832. The largest and tallest of these was built on a block of stonework embedded in a slag heap 60 feet high. The stack itself was another 240 feet high above ground, so tall as to be a landmark for ships making their way into Swansea harbour.

Local farmers from the Tawe Valley brought an action against John Henry and Richard Hussey Vivian regarding damage to their farms. Their solicitor advised them to ask for 'reasonable compensation' but they had always been refused. Grand juries at Cardiff and Cowbridge refused the Bills of Indictment, but in 1833 such a bill was accepted at Carmarthen. The farmers were represented at the Carmarthen Quarter Sessions in March 1833 by Thomas David of Llansamlet. Sir James Scarlett K.C., a former Attorney General, represented the Vivians, while John Evans, a comparatively unknown barrister from Merthyr Tydfil, represented Thomas David and his fellow farmers. A number of witnesses appeared in court, all with more or less the same tale to tell. One of them, Thomas Hopkins, introduced a new word to the Welsh language: *efryddod*, a crippling disease affecting animals, cattle in particular, who suffered the effects of harmful copper smoke.

For the defence, William Bevan and others refuted any claim of harm done by the smoke. Their testimony was bolstered by more testimony from Doctors George Gwynne Bird and Edward Howell.

The jury promptly made their minds up and were ready at almost midnight on the day of the hearing to relay their verdict, but Judge Patterson had a duty to explain what a 'public nuisance' entailed according to the Law. As he sat down the jury foreman stood up to say that they had reached a verdict of Not Guilty. Two members begged to differ but were persuaded to change their minds after a re-think. Had a guilty verdict been delivered, it would have had far-reaching implications and consequences, but the owners were pleased – indeed, so pleased that church bells were rung almost all day in Swansea to celebrate the saving of the copper industry.

In August 1834 another complaint, this time against the Grenfells and the Middle Bank Copper Works was brought, and a claim for £3,000 damages made at a case heard at the Breconshire Assizes. Many of the witnesses that had appeared at Carmarthen were called to testify. A cow and a horse suffering from *efryddod* symptoms were taken to Brecon as evidence. The trial lasted for fourteen hours. The jury deliberated for forty-five minutes, but their verdict did not please Thomas David or any of his friends. Despite acknowledging the fact that his farm had suffered from smoke effect, the jury said that most of his losses were due to poor farming on his part and awarded him an insulting 1 shilling for damages.

Despite the fact that there was clear evidence of smoke damage to animals and vegetation, a number of supposedly intelligent people were not convinced of any ill effects on humans and tried their best to persuade the public that smoke did them very little harm. A letter by 'Medicus' appeared in the *Cambrian* newspaper on 23 March 1822 implying that Swansea was a healthy place to live in, as persons such as Catherine Thomas had spent most of her 103 years living by the White Rock Copper Works; Jane Miles of Pentrechwith lived to be 107 years old and David Job, ninety-eight years old, had lived all his life near the Upper Bank Works. No better testimony could be asked for. Fever and croup had affected many in the town but none of the residents of the copper smelting districts had suffered. Asthma and bronchitis may well have been caused by extreme changes of temperature at the works!

The reality of the situation was shown in a Royal Commission Report in 1843 in which facts were used to portray the realities of life and death for copper workers and their families. Sir Henry de la Beche concluded his report by asking, 'How can one expect that smoke virulent enough to scour window glass, and change within a few hours the colour of convolvulus, would not damage human tissue?'

Even so, Thomas Williams, a Swansea surgeon of the highest reputation, had his eyes clouded by the smoke and could not see the damage all around him. He spoke publicly of, and repeated in writing, the beneficial effects of the smoke. As another letter writer to the *Cambrian* mildly suggested on 8 December, 1854, 'Dr. Thomas Williams is in the land of dreams.'[10] Poor Dr Tom's brains must have been addled by an overdose of smoke as he was convinced that Swansea's problem was that there was not *enough* smoke in the atmosphere!

Thankfully not everyone was as deluded. Swansea's first Medical Officer of Health, Dr William Henry Michael, was a far more sensible man who laboured to ensure that the

Local Government Act of 1856 was adhered to in Swansea. The Act contained a clause which stated that all furnaces and fireplaces had to be built with the ability to eradicate smoke. Unfortunately the Act did not apply to the smelting of ores, but Michael still held to his beliefs that clean air was to everyone's benefit.

Though the smoke was ever-present, the results of the Carmarthen and Brecon trials, which were not favourable to claimants, meant that few dared to stand up to the copper smelters for a period of twenty-five years. Then Dugdale Houghton, a Birmingham land agent and surveyor, inherited property in between the Nedd and Afan rivers. His lands included the Fforchdwm estate at Blaen Pelena and Coed yr Iarll Uchaf, Coed yr Iarll Isaf and Cwrt y Bettws farms near the mouth of the Nedd. In 1853, the Red Jacket Copper Works had a dozen working furnaces to its name and another two or three in preparation. Smoke killed animals on Coed yr Iarll farms, and Houghton asked for damages at the Carmarthen Summer Assizes in July 1858.

Swansea-born William Grove, a scientist and barrister, was counsel for Dugdale Houghton in his claim against Frederick Bankart, owner of the copper-smelting Red Jacket Works. Houghton had lost 400 sheep and two horses, all suffering from swollen tongues and heads, ulcerated jaws, tumours in the throat, enlarged joints and brittle bones – all classic signs of the dreaded *efryddod*. His crops and pastures had all failed and he asked for £864 damages. Jacob Williams, the previous tenant, spoke on his behalf and outlined the problems he had faced while farming Coed yr Iarll. After a three-day trial the jury retired for half an hour and returned with a suggestion that Houghton be paid £450 damages. This was the first substantial award to anyone who had claimed damages, and was taken as a victory for small farmers over copper barons.

Dugdale Houghton tried again in 1859 and won from the Britton Ferry Copper Works a further £1,200 in compensation for losses. In 1860 Houghton took the Red Jacket Copper Works to court again for losses incurred at Cwrt y Bettws farm. This time the award was only £150. Houghton could not afford any more litigation and moved from Wales to Dowles Manor, Worcestershire, in 1868.

His victories, however small, were a spur to others. Nash Vaughan sued the English Copper Company. They yielded before a trial could begin and agreed to take reasonable steps to eradicate the problem of smoke, and if Nash Vaughan was not satisfied with the improvement after two years, an appeal could be made to the Board of Trade. Vaughan died within two years and the copper works went back to their old methods.

The name Rio Tinto was a familiar one for Anglesey residents in the late twentieth century as it was connected to an aluminium smelting works on the island, but for residents of Cwmafan the company was, at one time, the bane of their lives.

In 1890, tenants of the Margam Estate complained to the estate owner, Lady Emily Talbot, of damage to their animals and crops from smoke from Stac y Foel. Lady Talbot had hay and soil samples tested that were found to be heavily polluted by sulphur. She had sheep tested and their intestines were found to contain large quantities of copper. She also knew that under the 1881 Alkali Act factories should, to the best of their abilities, use all and any means to eradicate smoke and gases from their works. She served an injunction on the Rio Tinto Company. They defended the action and said that to comply fully with the act would mean the works being transferred to Spain, resulting in a loss of jobs for many of the area's workforce and a loss to the economy. Lady Talbot decided against pursuing her claim and accepted payment of £1,400 and further annual payments of £700.

Others followed suit, and the Rio Tinto Company offered compensation ranging from £30 to £100. One farmer, tenant of a farm near Tonmawr in the Afan valley, asked for £650, only to be offered ten guineas, which was subsequently raised to seventy-five guineas. William Rees and Hugh Morrison sued the company for more at the Glamorgan Summer Assizes held at Swansea in 1895. Rees testified in Welsh, only to suffer bigotry and intolerance from J. C. Bigham, counsel for the defence. Despite being insulted, William Rees, much to his credit, carried on testifying in Welsh and was supported by Edward Rees, who had lost almost all of a flock of 1,300 sheep to the effects of the smoke. Dr Monroe, a scientist, had examined a dead sheep and found that its spleen contained five grains of copper, which he considered an 'enormous' amount. An estimate of £555 5s. was also given by him of William Rees' losses over a period of seven years at Fforchlas farm in the Creggan Valley.

Testifying for the Rio Tinto Company were a works manager and a chemist. When offered the opportunity to taste scrapings off a stone which had come from half a mile from the stack at Cwmafan furnaces, the chemist was forced to admit that the scrapings did indeed contain copper. Others were called to testify but little truth was spoken in court.

The trial lasted for six days and closed with a two-hour speech by J. C. Bigham, who was not the most electrifying speaker at the best of times. He was convinced, and tried his very best to convince everyone else, that gases from the works chimney stacks offered no risk to vegetation.

Judge Lawrence reminded the jury that they only had

two questions to consider: whether or not the farmers had suffered as a result of the smoke, and was the problem better or worse that it was twenty-five years before? He also reminded them that as the company had already made payments to Lady Talbot, it was only right that Morrison and Rees be compensated as well. After five and a half hours they agreed that there had been no increase in the amount of smoke that billowed over the valley, but they disagreed over what compensation should be paid and therefore could not give a verdict.

The trial was adjourned. Rio Tinto carried on for a further eleven years before relocating to Spain. The Cwmafan Works was closed. This was the beginning of the end. By 1921 every other copper smelter in the Tawe Valley had closed.

[1] *Copper Mountain.* John Rowlands. (Anglesey Antiquarian Society, 1981).
[2] *Mynydd Parys: A Strategy for Humanities.* G. T. Jones. (University College of North Wales, 1987).
[3] 'Yellow Fever in Swansea, 1865'. P. D. Meers, *Journal of Hygiene.* (Cambridge, 1986).
[4] *Exploring the Wild Welsh Coast.* Stuard D. Ludlum (ed.). *Harper's New Monthly Magazine* (1883).
[5] *Ibid.*
[6] *Wales 100 Years Ago.* Richard Lovett (ed.). (The Religious Tract Society, 1892).
[7] *Wild Wales.* George Borrow. (Collins, 1862).
[8] 'The South Wales copper-smoke dispute, 1833–95'. Ronald Rees. *(Cylchgrawn Hanes Cymru, 1981).*
[9] *King Copper: South Wales and the Copper Trade 1584–1895.* Ronald Rees. (University of Wales Press).
[10] *Ibid..*

21

Troubles and strikes

At Parys Mountain and Amlwch, weekly wages were on average between 6 and 8 shillings per week, compared to the 3 to 5 shillings a week paid to miners in Cornwall. Cornish mines were making only small profits, whilst the Anglesey mines' profits were much bigger. This scale of profits was not, however, reflected in wages for the miners in Wales, but rather in gains for the owners. Despite their protestations, in fact the miners were much better paid than the farm workers of the time: they received up to £11 more annually.

It is believed that the Plas Newydd and Llys Dulas families of Anglesey were able to bank up to £300,000 profits in the period between 1770 and 1800. Owen Griffith said that the difference between the miners' wages and the owner's profits was comparable to the difference between a fly and an archangel.

On the whole, agents or mine managers were an unpopular lot due to their methods of dealing and setting bargains; and, because they were mostly English incomers, there were linguistic differences to take into account.

The 'bargains' system was unpopular and often unfair. A group of four to six workers (tributers) would be set the work of digging/mining ore for a price agreed between their leader and the agent. Prices were set per ton per quarter and would have to be adhered to – whether the bargain was good or bad, fair or unfair.

Following a poor harvest in 1816, and subsequently high food prices, Plas Newydd rents were reduced, as the tenants couldn't pay the rents as well as sustain their families on the wages paid to them. The workers believed that if the

Anglesey grain was not exported, local prices would come down and they could afford to live a little better. They went on strike in their call for more pay, but their pleas were unanswered. The mine owners offered only £300 to a Relief Fund when at least £2,000 was needed to buy food for the townspeople.

In February 1817 the *Wellington* (Captain John Hughes) was at anchor at Amlwch Port ready to sail with a cargo of local grain to Liverpool. A group of men boarded the ship and stole the rudder, which they hid in Llanwenllwyfo churchyard. The militia were recalled from Ireland to quell the riots. Six of the ringleaders were arrested. The rudder was returned. Other leaders were jailed, whilst the rest returned to Amlwch in triumph amidst scenes of jubilation.

There is no doubt that there were miners from the mountain's workforce amongst the protesting crowds, and James Treweek had to battle hard to keep them under control. There were complaints about the low wages, and a visit to Plas Newydd was threatened to discuss or plead with the mine owner. In time, the protest petered out.

In 1819 William Morgan and seventeen other smelters put in an application for a rise in pay. All they asked for was an extra two shillings a day. After being threatened with arrest, they all returned to work.

A dispute arose in 1820 regarding having to work on Sundays. Despite their rough outward appearance most of the miners were regular chapel- or churchgoers, and being able to worship on the Sabbath was a matter of faith and principle to them. Underground prayer meetings were held at the beginning and end of every shift at six o'clock in the morning and between nine and ten o'clock at night. If they worked the eight-hour night shift, they were able to attend both services.

In 1825 the workers made a plea for better working

conditions. Feelings ran so high that fifty extra men were employed to guard both the works and the workers who did not support the strike.

Another unsuccessful application for more wages was made in 1846, but the workers were forced to return to work as they could not afford to continue the strike:

> The miners 'turned out' for wages on Monday and remained out until Wednesday, when their demands not being complied with they resumed their work. They conducted themselves in a peaceable and orderly manner.[1]

By 1860 the company was suffering financial problems and could not afford to pay the workers the rate that had been agreed upon. Prayer meetings were held and guidance sought from above, but an impatient workforce became more militant as they couldn't make ends meet on what they were paid. Families were in dire straits; children suffered; savings dwindled. As we saw earlier, during the dispute the works manager, Captain Tiddy, had to hide in the Engine Room. The engine had worked perfectly for years without any problems, but one night when Tiddy was seeking shelter it exploded! The poor man must have thought that the Day of Reckoning had arrived. The dispute of 1860 saw the ending of the bargaining system and Thomas Tiddy was forced to leave the mine.

Another story from the same dispute concerns the owners having to seek shelter in the office as they did not have enough ready cash to pay what they owed the workforce. The men took pity on them after a few hours and let them go. As one of the owners rushed from the site on horseback, a strong gust of wind closed the yard gates, trapping the horse and rider between the two halves of the gate. The rider had to plead to be set free.

A dispute arose in 1863 because the local Welsh workers were under the impression that some of the imported Cornish workforce, Thomas and William Buzza in particular, were being shown favouritism by Captain George Trewren. Owen Roberts, leader of the Welsh workers, lost his job, and only when he was reinstated did the others agreed to return to work. The Buzza brothers felt that they had suffered humiliation in 'the foul and shameful treatment we have received on different occasions from the mob'.[2] The brothers returned to Cornwall.

There were conflicts in the south Wales copper works as well. In 1768 a dispute arose at the Forest Copper Works. Robert Morris, the owner, had so little faith in his workforce that he brought in others from Pembrokeshire to take their place, and he even built a block of flats as accommodation for them. There is no information as to the reaction of the local people to these 'strike-breakers'.

A thousand Swansea copper workers protested in 1843 that they had been forced to accept a 12 per cent cut in wages because of falling profits. The employers' argument was that they were still better off and better paid than any other workers! After a speech (and probably a sermon) by the Reverend Thomas Davies, minister of Pentre Chapel, they all went back to work, but within a fortnight there were other strikes at Hafod, White Rock, Middle Bank, Neath and Briton Ferry copper works. The *Cambrian* newspaper of 11 August 1843 reported:

We are sorry to state that the workmen of the Swansea Copper Works stopped work this morning, declining to submit to the proposed reduction in their wages. The men engaged in the following extensive works have stood out – Messrs Vivian's, Messrs. Williams, Porter and Co's, the Middle Bank Works, the Whiterock Works, the Upper Bank, the Crown Copper Works, Neath, and the Red Jacket Copper Works, Neath. Those in the employ of the Messrs. BENSON have not struck.

The men of one of the works had assembled about ten o'clock this morning,in a field above the Hafod Works, where they expected to be joined by the others, when they were to go in procession through Morriston, and all the Works, and perhaps through Swansea. The following are the reductions complained of: Slagmen, formerly earning 30s a week, are now reduced to 22s 6d.; metal smelters, from 30s to 26s 3d.; ore smelters, from 26s to 22s 6d.; roasters, from 31s 6d. to 27s 6d.; middle calciners, from 2s 4d. to 2s 2d. per watch; and ore calciners, from 2s 2d to 2s per watch.[3]

[1] *North Wales Chronicle,* 26 May 1846.
[2] *Copper Mountain.* John Rowlands. (Anglesey Antiquarian Society, 1981).
[3] *Cambrian* newspaper, 11 August 1843.

22

Pounds and pence; coins and tokens

Thomas Williams was a man brimming with ideas. When he realised that the Royal Mint's copper coinage was of poor quality and easy to counterfeit, he decided to produce his own coins/tokens to pay his employees. However, he was not the first to have such thoughts. What is known as the Halsall Penny, possibly produced by Matthew Boulton for Colonel Mordaunt's cotton mill in Halsall, Lancashire, is regarded as the first copper token of the Industrial Revolution.

In the past, various rulers of Wales (or areas of Wales) had minted coins, and banknotes had been a familiar part of Welsh life for a few years – in Aberystwyth in 1762 *Banc y Llong* (the Ship Bank) was founded, with its own notes. Later in the same century cattle drovers set up banks in central Wales, issuing their own notes. Coins, however, were a different matter.

The idea of minting his own coins first came to Williams in 1786. By March 1787, Parys Mine Company tokens, known by collectors as Druids, were in circulation. These were accepted as being of such good design and high quality that Williams, and his co-producer Mathew Boulton, considered making an offer to produce coinage for the Royal Mint.

By March 1787 London newspapers carried articles about the new coinage that was being used at the great copper mine on the Isle of Anglesey. The blank discs were prepared at Greenfield, Flintshire, before being sent on to be pressed at Great Charles Street, Birmingham, and there cut and finished. The 'heads' side or front of the coins showed a Druid encircled with a wreath of oak leaves; on the 'tails' or reverse side was the cipher of the Parys Mine Company with the promise to pay the bearer one penny. On the rim were the words: 'On demand in London, Liverpool and Anglesey'.

The coins were designed by John Gregory Hancock the Elder. Despite his work being of a very high standard, he was often ridiculed and belittled in the press. A satirical verse was printed in the *Gentleman's Magazine* in 1792:

The artist paused awhile in great suspence
To make a penny of some consequence,
And having Stukeley or old Dugdale read,
Stamp'd the pittance with a Druid's head;
To make his own resemblance next he tried,
And struck a cypher on the counterside.[1]

At first only penny tokens were produced, but in 1788 halfpenny tokens were minted. Those, like the Royal Mint's coins, proved easy to forge. Only pennies dated 1787–1791 and halfpennies dated 1788-1791 are considered genuine. A total of 8,960,000 (250 tons) of pennies, each containing an ounce of copper, and 3,584,000 (50 tons) of halfpennies were produced. They remained in legal use until 1818.

From 1788 onwards all tokens for the Parys Mine Company (PMC) were produced in Birmingham by Mathew Boulton; he continued to do so until 1798 when he concentrated on producing coinage for the Royal Mint. Many of the later coins for the PMC were special editions.

The 1790 halfpennies that were struck at Soho by Matthew Boulton were the world's first modern coins, round in shape and of a regular size and weight.

When production of coins at the Parys Mine Mint in

Great Charles Street, Birmingham, was stopped by Thomas Williams, Boulton took over production of Druid halfpennies in 1789, using the presses previously used by Williams and with Hancock's engraved dies.

Boulton commissioned the French engraver Rambert Dumarest to produce a Druid-head pattern for the Anglesey pieces. Two slightly different heads were produced. Boulton was of the opinion that the first of them was not good enough, because the design had so little relief that it would quickly wear away. Remedying the situation took time, and Williams was unhappy that he had to wait until October 1790 for the changes to be made. He was unaware that machinery at the Mint, where they were to be struck, was also being altered and changed. Despite the changes made, Williams was still not satisfied with the designs or the samples he saw. He wrote an angry letter to Boulton on 31 October 1790 to complain. He was much happier with the designs that Hancock had used and insisted on those. Though Boulton and Williams fell out over the coins, Boulton carried on using designs by Dumarest for coins/tokens for the Cornish Metal Company owned by John Vivian.

Not only did Thomas Williams venture into the minting process, he also set up his own bank. He went into partnership with the Reverend Edward Hughes and his son H. R. Hughes to open the Chester and North Wales Bank in 1792, with branches in Chester, Caernarvon and Bangor. In 1797 the bank experienced difficulties and was forced to close until it restabilised. Other family members and new partners took over after Williams' death in 1802 until the bank was taken over by Lloyd's.

Where one leads, others follow. South Wales copper works issued coins and tokens to their workers in the same way that Thomas Williams had minted the Anglesey pennies and halfpennies. Grant Francis (1814–1882), the historian who was one of the founding members of the Royal Institution for South Wales, a society to promote Swansea's history, had in his possession a large collection of such coins. Amongst the earliest were a halfpenny and a farthing dated 1666, made of brass. These may well have been coins of legal tender but were stamped with, possibly, the owners' initials.

Few, if any, copper works tokens were issued after 1814, though those that had been issued were still in use until 1825. Between 1830 and 1865 brass, copper and gilt tokens, which were termed 'cheques', of the value of ¼d, ½d, 1½d, 2d, and 3d were issued and welcomed by taverns, so enticing thirsty workers on their way home from their shift, and where they could be exchanged for beer of the same value.

By 1845 the Taibach Copper Works was minting coins not only for itself but also for the government of the Malay States.[2]

[1] *Copper Mountain.* John Rowlands. (Anglesey Antiquarian Society, 1981).
[2] *The Smelting of Copper in the Swansea District of South Wales from the Time of Queen Elizabeth to the Present Day.* Grant Francis. (Henry Sotheran & Co, 1881).

23

The legacy of the copper industry

One notable feature of modern-day Parys Mountain is the peacefulness one feels on walking its paths and yet, in the quietness, one might feel a shiver of thrill from the past. No one can deny the mountain's busy past – the signs are ever-present – but one unseen sign was an underground lake which until fairly recently posed a threat to the future of the old workings and to the town of Amlwch. But as it was a case of 'out of sight, out of mind' few had ever given it much thought.

A feature of early twenty-first century weather in the United Kingdom has been very heavy rainfall with extreme flooding in some places. In 2003 flooding became a real threat to Amlwch: not just because of the weather, but because of rainwater that had collected over decades to form that huge underground lake inside Parys Mountain.

During the 1950s a concrete dam had been built in the mountain's Adda Valley adit to restrain acidic water. Together with natural rainwater penetrating through the rocks a lake of about 50,000 cubic litres had formed behind it. According to some reports, it was of the constitution of a weak car battery acid and of a burgundy colour! It was also continuously corroding the concrete that was supposed to retain it. In fact it had a pH level of about 2.5 and was clear. Had the corroded dam been fractured by the pressure of the water behind it, a real danger of extreme flooding and pollution in Amlwch would have had to be faced. It was an environmental disaster waiting to happen, and the age and condition of the dam meant that it could happen at any time.

A Dewatering Project Group was set up consisting of members of Parys Underground Group, Amlwch Industrial Heritage Trust, Anglesey Mining plc, the Welsh Development Agency, the Countryside Commission for Wales and Anglesey County Council. A grant of £20,000 facilitated the work of the Cementation Civil Engineering Company to examine the dam and the draining of the lake. It took a period of six weeks to pump the lake dry and relieve the pressure on the dam and on Amlwch residents. Thirty million gallons of waste water, at the rate of fifty litres per second, were pumped out of the lake into Afon Goch Dulas, saving Amlwch from potential disaster.

The polluted lake water was nothing compared to what was already in the river. This comparatively small river is one of the worst carriers of poisonous metals flowing into the Irish Sea. The level of the water in the underground lake fell 70 metres and an entrance to some of the old, unexplored workings of the Mona Mine was gained. Now all waste water flows down the Adda Valley adit into Afon Goch Amlwch.

Mining at Parys Mountain ceased in 1917, but re-examination of the works has taken place since 1955, with more than one company hoping to mine bluestone (a combination of copper, lead and zinc sulphides). Though the ore was found, there was not sufficient quality or quantity to make it a commercial success. The Anglesey Copper Mines (UK) Ltd Company drilled eleven trial shafts up to 1962 but did not find success. For a period of four years from 1966 onwards the Canadian Industrial Gas & Oil Company Ltd (CIGOL) drilled fifty-two trial shafts, again with no luck.

In 1973 copper, lead, zinc and a little gold and silver were discovered, and the Morris Shaft commenced on 11

October 1988. Following more research by the Anglesey Mining Co. Ltd (AMCL) in 1984 it was found that up to 4.5 million tons of ore could be mined. Permission was sought from the county council in May 1986 to further develop the work on the mountain. The council granted their request after a six-month consideration period, but conditions regarding historical buildings and areas of scientific interest were set.

Planning permission was granted in 1988 so the company could begin work to offset financial problems. At that time, world zinc prices were high and hopes were raised, only to be later disappointed. The company searched for a supply of copper and zinc, hoping they might come across some gold and silver. It was also hoped that ore prices in general would rise so more capital could be gained to invest in the work on Parys Mountain. An Australian company was approached to invest in mining and employing more men. Again, nothing came of the venture. World copper prices rose in the early years of the twenty-first century, so between 2005 and 2008 AMCL focused their attention on the easterly Garth Daniel and the westerly Graig Wen regions of the mountain in expectation of mining up to 1,000 tons of ore per day.

Problems had to be faced during the recession of 2008, and the company failed to come to terms with Western Metals Limited, Perth, Australia, regarding the sale and purchase of the site. The venture was abandoned in October 2008. At present (2012), there appears to be very little activity there, and the AMC plc is still waiting on a recovery in the world of mining in general before committing themselves any further into restarting their efforts on Parys Mountain.

An article appeared in *Private Eye* magazine in 1990 strongly suggesting that further use of the site was being considered. It was suggested that the tunnels and chambers of the mountain could be used as a storage place for nuclear waste materials. The benefits of the site were listed as:

- An ideal geographically-situated site – apart from one other site in central England that would never be seriously considered. It was said that only on Parys Mountain, on Llŷn peninsula and in Scotland were suitably safe rock formations found.
- Parys Mountain is close to the coast with harbour facilities at nearby Amlwch Port and deep water facilities at Wylfa, where a nuclear power station is already situated.
- Amlwch and Parys Mountain are close to other transport facilities such as roads (A55) and railways (old Amlwch/Gaerwen branch line ripe for development and re-opening to connect with the main Holyhead/Crewe/London line).
- Being close to the existing Wylfa Nuclear Power Station, whose working life is coming to an end – though serious consideration is being given to Wylfa B.

So far, nothing more has been heard of any such plans so Anglesey residents have to sit, wait and see.

Other developments have been announced. In March 2010, a national Lottery award of £470,000 was earmarked for the Amlwch Industrial Heritage to develop plans for The Copper Kingdom, which will centre attention on the tourist/visitor trade. Guides are being trained who will explain the historical relevance of Parys Mountain and Amlwch Port. There will be walking tours around the industrial buildings' remains. Old local crafts will be redeveloped, and people will be trained in preservation skills. All of this will hopefully ensure a safe future for what had appeared to be in danger of being lost and forgotten. Amlwch's future now relies on regeneration.

Edward Greenly (1861–1951) maintained that there were two wildernesses on Anglesey: one, the sandy coastline of Llanddwyn and Newborough, which was created by Nature; the other, Parys Mountain which was created by man and made so unpleasant. The author Bobi Jones, however, found an enthralling beauty in the mountain's various colours of black, blue, red and yellow. Other colours are gradually re-appearing on the mountain, such as the purple heather, red foxglove, yellow gorse, grey lichen and almost 200 other plants. Crows, choughs and jackdaws are regular sights, as are many other smaller birds. Creatures such as the adder are regularly seen; so much wildlife that there are seven biological Sites of Special Scientific Interest on Parys Mountain. Erasmus Darwin (Charles' grandfather), one of the first naturalists to visit the mountain in 1790, would surely be pleased: he noted a lichen (lichens benefit from pure air) was growing there then; now even more lichens are being studied on the mountain's rocks and stones with a view to plotting the cleanliness of the air in the twenty-first century. There are also five geological SSSIs on the mountain.

Because of the 466 other features of archaeological interest and six Scheduled Ancient Monuments (the Great Opencast, the five-sailed windmill, Pearl Shaft engine house, Central precipitation pits, Adda Valley reverberatory furnace and the Mona Smelting site), the mountain has been designated a Landscape of Outstanding Historic Significance and is in consideration for inclusion on the European Route of Industrial Heritage in the United Kingdom. It may even be considered as a World Heritage Site in the near future.

At the beginning of the twentieth century, Swansea faced a future without a copper industry. All the factors that had been responsible for establishing the industry in South Wales were by then looking less important as other countries found they could provide for themselves what Swansea alone had offered in the past.

New coal sources discovered near to the supply of much richer copper ores in North and South America and Australia meant that smelting plants were being set up in those locations. Less and less ore came to Wales and the cost of importing it became prohibitive. Many skilled workers moved from Wales in search of a better future. In 1906, the Rio Tinto company moved to Spain as it had threatened to do so in 1895. By 1921 every furnace was cold. The Welsh method of smelting was considered old-fashioned. The New World wanted New Methods.

Cardiff had increased in size. In many aspects of everyday life it had also grown in importance over Swansea. Swansea faced an uncertain future. Foreign competition for the copper smelters forced them to consider a future dealing with other non-ferrous metals.

The last copper smelting company in Wales held out until 1891, when the Yorkshire Imperial Metals Company closed down at the Hafod Copper Works site. Today, all that remains of Copperopolis is a 12½-acre site waiting to be redeveloped as part of an industrial centre, with fourteen listed structures including a canal, traces of a narrow gauge railway, a locomotive shed, a laboratory building, a rolling mill and two engine houses, one of which still retains its steam engine.

The Hafod Copper Works Regeneration Project concentrates on what was possibly the most important industrial site in the Swansea Valley. Close by are another 159 internationally significant copper-related buildings or structures, which can be used as a focus of research in Science, Technology, Engineering and Mathematics, as well as in Social Sciences, Arts and Humanities. Such a project could also be used to transform the area's economy, society, culture, landscape, physical environment, and marine environment. Few other sites, if any, anywhere in the world, offer such possibilities. The City and County of Swansea have plans for the future of the Hafod/Morfa copper workks site to enable people to live in, work in, and visit this most important of sites. Swansea University is also working with the City and County of Swansea to explore regeneration opportunities for the site. For the lower Swansea Valley area, the future is bright.

Two hundred years ago, the Swansea valley was a hive of industrial activity, but by 1961 almost all of the activity in the valley had ceased, and a landscape of industrial decay – the remains of derelict works and mills, spoil heaps and severe pollution – was left behind. The Lower Swansea Valley Project was led by Swansea Council and other interests after World War Two, to remove the industrial dereliction and pollution of the valley and return the area to active use. Events such as the 200th anniversary of the founding of the Hafod copper works in Swansea were celebrated in 2010. The same year was the fiftieth anniversary of the establishment of the Lower Swansea Valley Project.

Swansea's almost forgotten past is gradually coming back to life again. The Lower Swansea Valley is being promoted as the 'Global and Local World of Welsh Copper' in a project based at Swansea University and funded by the Economic and Social Research Council, and supported by the City and County of Swansea, University of Glamorgan, National Museum Wales, and the Royal Commission on the

Ancient and Historical Monuments of Wales. Such work will put Swansea's industrial sites on a par with other World Heritage Sites in Wales.

Similar projects are to take place in Amlwch. The Greenfield Heritage Park already exists in Clwyd.

Towards the end of the twentieth century, the Great Orme Country Park was opened. This contained the remains of the three Great Orme copper mines. The Bronze Age Copper Mine is now a major tourist attraction. Together with a visitors' centre and an opportunity to see the inside of some of the workings, it provides a link with the area's past to present day visitors and can claim to be the only tourist attraction/major archaeological site to have won a Guinness World Record (awarded in May 2004) as it is considered the largest Bronze Age copper mine in the world.

The area known as 'Happy Valley' on the Great Orme was presented by Lord Mostyn to the townspeople of Llandudno to celebrate Queen Victoria's Golden Jubilee. It was landscaped and developed as formal gardens. Lawns, two miniature golf courses, a putting green and an open air theatre were added. Ceremonies connected with the National Eisteddfod were held there in 1896 and in 1963. In June 1969 a cabin lift was built to the summit of Great Orme and, like the tramway, provides an interesting way to view the Great Orme. The Happy Valley Entertainers Open Air Theatre was closed in 1985, and the golf courses removed to make space for an artificial ski slope. Much-needed restorative work was made on the gardens to celebrate the Millennium.

Like all other aspects of Welsh history, the copper industry in Wales is chronicled for future reference. The glories of the past must be kept for posterity.

Museum information

(This information is correct at the date of publication.)

Oriel Môn
Rhosmeirch
Llangefni
Anglesey
LL77 7TQ
01248 724444
www.visitanglesey.co.uk
Daily 10.30 am – 5 pm
Admission free

Plas Newydd
Llanfair Pwllgwyngyll
Anglesey
LL61 6DQ
01248 714795
email:
plasnewydd@nationaltrust.org

**Amlwch Copper Kingdom/
Sail Loft Visitor Centre**
The Old Sail Loft
Amlwch Port
Anglesey
LL68 9DB
01407 832255
www.copperkingdom.co.uk

Llandudno Copper Mine
Great Orme Mine
Llandudno
Conwy LL30 2XG
01492 870447
e-mail: info@gomines.co.uk
www.greatormemines.info

Greenfield Valley Heritage Park
Administration Centre
Basingwerk House
Greenfield Valley
Greenfield, Holywell
Flintshire CH8 7GH
01352 714172
info@greenfieldvalley.com
www.greenfieldvalley.com

National Waterfront Museum
Oystermouth Road
Maritime Quarter
Swansea SA1 3RD
01792 638950
e-mail:
waterfront@museumwales.ac.uk
www.museumwales.ac.uk
Open 10 am – 5 pm
Admission free

Swansea Museum
Victoria Road
Maritime Quarter
Swansea SA1 1SN
01792 653763
Open all year, Tuesday–Sunday:
10 am – 5 pm
(Last admission 4.40 pm);
closed Mondays
except Bank Holiday Mondays
Admission free
www.swansea.gov.uk/swanseamuseum

Glossary

(Terms used in this book and in Further Reading)

ADIT (ADDIT)   horizontal tunnel or Level for draining the mine or for access

AGENT   mine manager

AIR DOOR   door fixed across a level to direct flow of air for ventilation

ANTIMONY   silvery, lustrous-grey metal usually found with sulphur, copper, lead and silver.

ARCHING   roof supports in a level built of stone, wood, concrete or iron

ASSAY OFFICE   where copper was graded according to its purity

BACKFILL   waste rock packed into a disused passage or stope

BARGAIN   task or work at an agreed payment with the captain of the mine

BARRACKS   building where miners ate, lived and slept at the mine

BING   an enclosure to keep and store ore

BLENDED ORE   a special type of ore

BOTTOMS   deepest part of the mine

BRIMSTONE   sulphur

BUDDLE   trough or circular pit where ore was separated from waste

CABAN   Welsh term for a recess cut into the rock underground for shelter.

CAKE   a copper ingot

CALCINE   to reduce to a powder

CAPE HORNERS   sailors who had sailed round Cape Horn on ore-carrying ships from South America to Swansea

CAPTAIN   honorary title, especially so in Cornwall, given to mine manager or mine foreman

CATCH PITS   precipitation pits for scrap metal. Called 'Pyllau Paent' (Paint Pits) in Amlwch

CENTER   the depth at which a level or adit would drain the mine

CHAIN LADDER   flexible ladder

CHILI BARS   roughly smelted Chilean copper ore

CLINKERS   a mass of incombustible slag which formed in the furnace

COPPER LADY   female mine worker who broke the ore into smaller pieces

COPPER PRECIPITATE   copper formed by action of acidic water on scrap metal

CRANCHES   pillars of rock supporting the roof of a mine

CROSS CUT	access tunnel, usually at right angle to main shaft, driven to cut the lode
CRUSHER	machine with two revolving drums to crush ore
CULVERT	escape route for smoke from smelting fires
DEADS	waste rock stacked in the roof or walls
DEBT	what was owed in the company stores and would be taken from wages. Sometimes the debt was more than the wages
DRESSING	the process of separating ore from waste material or producing slates
DRUMHOUSE	structure supporting the drum of a balanced incline
DÔL	Cornish term for valley. Welsh term for meadow
DUTIES	taxes.
EFRYDDOD	copper smoke-induced disease in animals
ENGINE SHAFT	shaft fitted with pumping equipment
FATHOM	6 feet unit of measurement
FIFTY-SIX	a metal weight – half a hundredweight
FIRESETTING	softening rock by heating with fire and then cooling it with water
FLAT RODS	iron or wooden rods transmitting motion from an engine to pumps
FLOP JACK	water powered engine using weight of water to operate a pump
FLUX	substance mixed with metals or ores to help in their melting and mixing
FOOTWAY	steps or stairs cut into rock face to facilitate moving from one level to another
FRENCH OCHRE	sediment used in paint-making
FURNACE, REVERBATORY	a furnace with a low roof, so the flame in passing to the chimney is deflected down onto the hearth, where the ores to be burned can be heated without coming into direct contact with the fuel.
FUSE	as long as possible to give everyone the opportunity to find shelter in the *caban*
GANGUE	crystalline minerals found in a lode with ore
GIN	winding engine
GIN CIRCLE	circle walked by a horse when working a gin
GINGING	stone lining to a shaft
GOSSAN	an oxide of iron and quartz and a sign of the presence of ore

GUESS — an estimate of the size of a heap to help calculate wages

HALVANERS — workers who would search the waste tips hoping to find something of value.

HONOUR — to work without pay

HOPPER — wooden storage bin holding rock thrown down from a stope

INCLINE — inclined underground level or surface track for access or haulage

BALANCED INCLINE — two parallel tracks with pulley wheel at top, where weight of full wagon descending pulled up empty wagon

CHAIN INCLINE — device running on chain or wire rope instead of rails

MASS-BALANCED INCLINE — single track with iron weight running between the rails to balance weight of down-going load

POWERED INCLINE — device where engine was used to haul loads upwards

TABLE INCLINE — where wagons were carried on a moving table rather than on the rails themselves

IRON PYRITES — 'fool's gold'

JUMPER — long iron rod, pointed at each end, which was used to drill shot holes by repeatedly hitting it against the rock face

KIBBLE — iron or wooden bucket for raising ore

KNOCKSTONE — small anvil (25cm x 20cm) used by Copper Ladies

LAPSTONE/ WHET-STONE — sharpening stone

LAUNDER — wooden trough for conveying water

LEACHING — recovering copper from an acidic solution by precipitation onto scrap iron

LEASE — an agreement concerning land or mining site

LEET — surface channel for conveying water

LEVEL — another term for an adit or tunne

LODE — metaliferous rock containing a deposit of ore

MILL — surface building where ore was processed

MOCHYN — Welsh term for the iron-weighted balancing trolley of a mass-balanced incline

OCHRE	an iron oxide used in paint-making
OLD MAN	the old miners or their workings
ON THE CARPET	being told off by one's betters or master
OPEN FRAKE	an opencast working
ORE	material from which metal could be extracted by smelting
OWNERS	mine owners
PACK WALL	waste rock stacked as a wall along side of level
PARTNERS	co-workers in a bargain
PELTON WHEEL	small waterwheel with cups into which a jet of water was directed
PILLAR	area of rock left undisturbed to support the roof
PITCHER	wide drill to drill open first hole
POWDER HOUSE	explosives store
REGULUS	ore bearing between eight and twelve per cent copper
RISE	underground shaft driven upwards to connect one gallery to another
SAMPLING HOUSE	where price of ore was set after it was checked for purity
SCORIA	slag used as a building material
SETT	area of a mining lease
SHAFT	vertical or slightly inclined entrance for access, haulage or pumping
SHEAVE	grooved pulley wheel
SHOADS	loose lumps of ore mixed with earth
SHOTHOLE	small diameter hole drilled into rock for inserting gunpowder
SILLS	a bed or layer of rock
SILVERS	silver coins, sometimes used in wages
SLAG	vitreous smelting refuse, clinkers
SLIDEWAY	unrailed incline
SPOIL	area of waste rock
SQUAT	semi-sitting position with one knee on ground
STAGING	platform set in side of a shaft
STEMPLE	wooden bar jammed between rock walls for climbing or supporting deads
STEWARD	works inspector
STOPE	underground working chamber
STORES	the company shop where all supplies had to be purchased from
STRING	a narrow vein of ore

| STRIKE | to find ore or to withhold labour in an industrial dispute |
| SUMP | underground shaft driven downwards |

TACK NOTE	an agreement to let a mine on condition that the owner is paid a proportion of the ore mined
TALLOW	candles made of animal fat
TALLY MAN	wages clerk - often an injured ex-miner
TRAMMER	usually young boys who were responsible for the trams to carry mined ore
TRIBUTER	miner who was paid an agreed sum for the ore removed
TRUNC	table of a table incline
TIMBLERS	large stones of ore
TUTWORK	non-productive work
TUTWORKMEN	underground workers

VEIN	a lode
VERDIGRIS	formed when cooper comes in contact with air; a light green colour
VIRGIN	very pure copper

WASTE	left-over material after ore has been removed from rocks
WATER ENGINE	a waterwheel driving pumps for drainage
WHIM	winding engine powered by horse, steam or water
WHIMSEY	steam-powered winding engine to raise ore or workers
WINCH	portable device for raising loads, either hand-, steam- or air-powered
WIND ENGINE	a windmill for driving drainage pumps
WINDLASS	hand-powered winch
WINZE	another term for a sump
WORKBAGS	to carry miner's tools, closed with a drawstring

| YARD | work place |
| YELLOW METAL | also known as Muntz metal. A brass alloy invented in 1832 by George Frederick Muntz. Contains a combination of copper (60 per cent) and zinc (40 per cent) + a small amount of iron. Cheaper than copper to produce but with the same qualities and as strong and reliable. Mainly used in industry and in shipping. Today it is used in the production of cheap but strong bolts. |

Some of the words that commonly occur in Welsh place-names

Aber = mouth of a river
Afon = river

Bod = abode/dwelling
Bryn = hill

Caer = fort
Capel = chapel
Carn = cairn
Carreg/cerrig = stone/stones
Cefn = ridge
Cil = nook
Coed = wood
C/Graig = rock
Cwm = valley

Dôl = meadow
Dyffryn = valley

Esgair = ridge

Glan = river bank/shore
Glyn = narrow valley

Hafod = summer home
Hendre = winter house
Heol = street

Llan = church or parish, usually, but not always, followed by a saint's name
Llwyn = bush
Llyn = lake
Llys = court

Maes = field
Melin = mill
Moel = bare/treeless
Mynydd = mountain

Nant = stream

Ogof = cave

Pant = valley
Pentref = village
Pen/ Penrhyn = promontory
Plas = palace
Pont = bridge
Porth = harbour

Rhyd = ford
Rhos = moorland

Tre = town

Tŷ/Tai = house/houses

Ynys = island
Ysgubor = barn
Ystrad = vale

Further Reading

'Anglesey Pattern Halfpence'. 'Copper and economic growth in Britain 1729-1784'. R. O. Roberts. *National Library of Wales Journal*, Summer 1857.

'Copper Smelting and Refining in the Eighteenth Century'. W. O. Alexander. *Murex Review* Vol. 1 No 15, 1955

'The Machynlleth Parc Copper Mine'. T. Morris. *Montgomeryshire Collections* Vol. 62 (1972)

'The Parys and Mona Copper Mines'. E. Cockshutt. *Transactions of the Anglesey Antiquarian Society* (1960)

'Yellow Fever in South Wales, 1865'. C. E. Gordon Smith & M. E. Gibson. *Medical History* (1986)

A Curious Place. The Industrial History of Amlwch (1550-1950). Bryan Hope. Bridge Books 1994.

A History of the Parishes of Whiteford and Holywell. Thomas Pennant (1798)

A List of Mines in Pembrokeshire and the adjoining parts of Carmarthen and Ceredigion. Peter Claughton, Dept. of History Exeter University April (1999)

A Short History of the Hafod Copperworks 1810-1924

A Wandering Scholar. The Life and Opinions of Robert Roberts. J. Burnett & H. G. Williams (University of Wales Press, 1991)

Archaeologia Cambrensis (1908)

Atgofion Ynyswr. Lewis Jones (Gwasg y Brython, 1939)

British Mining. Mason and Bevins (2002)

Bronze Age Copper Mining in Britain and Ireland. W. O'Brien (Shire Publications Ltd, 1996)

Chris Leather. (The Ormskirk and West Lancashire Numismatic Society website, 1970)

Copper Kingdom. P. Steele & R. Williams. Amlwch Industrial Heritage Trust 2011.

Copper Mountain. John Rowlands (Anglesey Antiquarian Society, 1981)

Copperopolis: landscapes of the early industrial period in Swansea. S. Hughes. (Royal Commission on Ancient and Historical Monuments in Wales, 2000)

Crwydro Sir y Fflint. T. I. Ellis (Llyfrau'r Dryw, 1959)

Cwm Tawe. Hywel Teifi Edwards (ed.) (Gwasg Gomer, 1993)

Cyffro Cymdeithasol Yng Nghymru 1800–c. 1843. Hugh Thomas

(University of Wales Press, 1972)
Exploring the Wild Welsh Coast. Stuart D. Ludlum (ed.) (Harper's New Monthly Magazine, 1883)
Ffurfiau'r Awen. W. Leslie Richards (Llyfrau'r Dryw 1963)
Great Orme Mines. C. J. Williams (Northern Mine Research Society 1995)
History of the Cardiganshire Mines. Absalom Francis (1874)
Journal of a Tour through North Wales. Arthur Aitkin (London, 1797)
King Copper – South Wales and the Copper Trade 1584-1895. Ronald Rees (University of Wales Press, 2000)
Lewis Morris – Plans in St. George's Channel, 1748. G. Budenberg (ed.) (Lewis Morris Productions, 1967)
Llandudno before the Hotels. C. Draper (Gwasg Carreg Gwalch, 2007)
Masts & Shafts. Eryl Wyn Rowlands (Amlwch Millennium Committee, 2000)
Metallurgy or the Art of Extracting Metals from their Ores, and Adapting them to various Purposes of Manufacture. John Percy (1864)
Mines of the Gwydyr Forest Part 7. J. Bennet & R. W. Vernon (Gwydyr Mines Publications, 1977)
Mona Antiqua Restaurata – An Archaeological Discourse on the Antiquities, Natural and Historical, of the Isle of Anglesey, the Antient Seat of the British Druids. Henry Rowlands. Dublin 1723.
Mynydd Parys. A Strategy for Humanities. G. T. Jones. UCNW 1987.
Mynydd Parys. Gwyn Parry and Steve Makin. Seren Books 1990.
Mynydd Parys. Owen Griffith. Cwmni'r Wasg Genedlaethol Gymreig Caernarfon. 1897.
Rhwng Môr a Mynydd. Ed.: Hugh Rees Ellis. Cyngor Gwlad Môn 1962.
Robert Owen Y Dre Newydd. R. O. Roberts (Y Clwb Llyfrau Cymraeg, 1948)
Saving Copperopolis. David Keys (BBC History magazine. August 2011)
Swansea Cape Horners Remember. (Swansea City Council – Maritime & Industrial Museum, undated)
Ten Days Through the Isle of Anglesea. Rev. John Skinner (December 1802)
The Dictionary of the Place-Names in Wales. H. W. Owen & R. Morgan (Gwasg Gomer, 2007)
The Great Orme Copper Mines. Don Smith (Creuddyn Publications, 1988)
The Smelting of Copper in The Swansea District Of South Wales From The Time Of Queen Elizabeth to the Present Day. Grant Francis (Henry

Sotheran & Co. 1881)

The Swansea Copper Barques and Cape Horners. Joanna Greenlaw (Published by the author, 1999)

The Twilight of Welsh Sail. Aled Eames (University of Wales Press, 1984)

Wales 100 Years Ago. Richard Lovett (ed.) (The Religious Tract Society, 1892)

Walk through South Wales, an account of a tour made in October 1819 by William and Sampson Sandys

Wild Wales. George Borrow (Collins 1862)

Also by J. Richard Williams

The story of convicts transported
from North Wales 1730-1878:

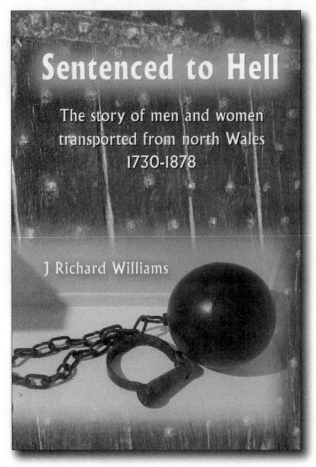

Gwasg Carreg Gwalch
www.carreg-gwalch.com